'I dressed for you!'

'I'm your boss. Th…

'I wouldn't count on it!' Rachel's voice tightened.

'Well, now,' Damian drawled softly, 'there's a challenge if ever I heard one. That's the third time you've put all your cards on the table! You'll never make a poker player, Miss Swift!' His eyes mocked her. 'Stick to looking beautiful and leave the intrigue to the big boys. I'd hate to see you completely beaten.'

Dear Reader

Friends can help make Christmas an extra-special time
for us all . . . so you can be sure that your friends at
Mills & Boon have chosen these four books especially
to enhance your enjoyment of the festive season. As all
good things should be, our novels are available all year
round, so why not make it your resolution to enjoy a
little romance every month of the coming year?

Happy Christmas,

The Editor

Sarah Holland was born in Kent and brought up in
London. She began writing at eighteen because she
loved the warmth and excitement of Mills & Boon. She
has travelled the world, living in Hong Kong, the South
of France and Holland. She attended a drama school,
and was a nightclub singer and a songwriter. She now
lives on the Isle of Man. Her hobbies are acting,
singing, painting and psychology. She loves buying
clothes, noisy dinner parties and being busy.

Recent titles by the same author:

RUTHLESS LOVER
CONFRONTATION
EXTREME PROVOCATION

UNGOVERNED PASSION

BY

SARAH HOLLAND

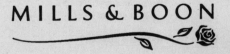

MILLS & BOON LIMITED
ETON HOUSE, 18-24 PARADISE ROAD
RICHMOND, SURREY TW9 1SR

For Hong Kong—the city I loved
and the people I knew there.

First published in Great Britain 1993
by Mills & Boon Limited

© Sarah Holland 1993

Australian copyright 1993
Philippine copyright 1993
This edition 1993

ISBN 0 263 78044 9

Set in 10 on 11½ pt Linotron Times
94-9311-54494

Typeset in Great Britain by Centracet, Cambridge
Made and printed in Great Britain

CHAPTER ONE

RACHEL spun in Tony's arms on the dance-floor. Her green eyes were shining, long black hair flying like a banner behind her as she moved, slender and graceful in a red dress. She loved dancing. It was one of the joys of life, and particularly she loved dancing tonight with Tony Radcliffe, because he was her oldest friend in the world and this was the first time she had seen him for eighteen months.

'Great dance!' she enthused, smiling at him. 'I've really missed you!'

'If you missed me so much, why did you leave Hong Kong?' Tony grinned, tall and blond and blue-eyed.

'I couldn't take the pressure any more.' Rachel had been born and brought up in Hong Kong, and dearly loved the colony. But her father and her uncle fought over her continually, dragging her into their lifelong feud, trying to get her to take sides. Two years ago, she had brought the whole thing to a halt by leaving Hong Kong and moving here, to London, to try to find some peace of mind.

Tony studied her sympathetically. 'It's still going on, you know. The fight between Charles and Jamie Swift. They're like two dogs with a bone.'

'They always will be,' Rachel said. 'I realised that in the end.' It had taken her twenty-two years, but in the end the truth had finally sunk in. Her uncle and her father were at war, and there was nothing she could do to stop it.

'Maybe this new guy will finally stop it,' said Tony suddenly, lifting blond brows.

'Who do you mean?' Rachel frowned.

'Damian Flint,' he said, and her lips parted.

'Ah, yes. . .' she replied.

Funnily enough, she could remember when she first heard that name. In a letter from Jamie. She had stared at it, struck by the combination of those two names: the dark romanticism of Damian and the ruthlessness of Flint. Yes, she had thought — a man with a name like that will be both tough and passionate, sensual yet at the same time sinister.

'What's he like?' she asked, sipping her drink.

'Women fall at his feet,' said Tony; 'power falls into his lap and money grows on the palm trees in his back garden. All in all, a thoroughly detestable individual!'

'Is it true he's after Swift?' Her father's company, Swift Investments, was an international finance house founded by her grandfather, and it was the bone that Charles and Jamie had fought over all their lives.

'It looks like it.' Tony shrugged. 'But don't worry about it. You left Hong Kong two years ago to get away from that particular mess. If Damian Flint takes it over — at least it'll end the war.'

Rachel gave a deep sigh. 'I feel guilty for leaving sometimes.'

Tony kissed her nose. 'You did the right thing, poppet. Come on — it's three o'clock in the morning. Let's go.'

They left the club, stepping out into the cool night air. It was July in London, and the city was alive. Tony hailed a black taxi sailing past and they leapt into the back. Rachel gave the address of her flat in Clapham, and the taxi shot away down the Old Brompton Road.

'How long are you in London for?' Rachel asked, her head on his shoulder as they drove.

'Another week.' Tony played with her black hair.

They had known each other since childhood, both the children of wealthy finance giants in Hong Kong. They were the same age — twenty-four — had been born and brought up in Hong Kong, and gone to school together. Once they had pretended they were child-hood sweethearts, played at falling in love, but of course it had all ended in laughter. They weren't lovers or sweethearts. They were just lifelong friends.

The taxi pulled into her street, the leafy shade of the trees sending dappled moonlight on to the long, sleek black bonnet of a chauffeur-driven Rolls-Royce limousine.

Tony whistled, studying the limousine. 'Wealthy neighbours!'

'Maybe it's my prince at last!' Rachel grinned, getting out of the taxi. 'Come up and say hello to Jenny! She was thrilled to hear you were in London!'

They went up the path to the Victorian house that contained her flat. Jenny was the girl she lived with, and the one who had given her the impetus to finally escape the suffocating love of her father and uncle in Hong Kong. She was a beautiful and intelligent woman in her late twenties, had worked as Jamie's secretary at Swift, and knew the family very well. She had also been completely in love with Jamie, but of course he had rejected her; there was no room in his life for love — not while he was consumed with hatred for his brother Charles.

'So you've been here for two years,' teased Tony as she looked for her key and opened the door, 'and still no boyfriend?'

Rachel went up the communal stairs. 'No one could replace you, Tony!' she teased.

He roared with laughter, tickling her. 'I'm your demon lover!'

'My one and only!' she giggled, opening the front door. 'The only man for me! The amazing, the delectable — Mr Tony Radcliffe!'

'The trendiest dude in all Hong Kong!' drawled Tony, and they both tumbled into the living-room in each other's arms, laughing like mad at their old joke.

There was an uncomfortable silence.

Jenny stood by the window, her face pale.

A man stood beside her, tall and formidable in a black Savile Row suit, hands thrust in trouser pockets, a gold watch-chain glittering across a formal waistcoat.

He had piercing blue eyes, hooded eyelids, a tanned, hard-boned face and a mouth so firm and uncompromising that Rachel felt a quiver go through her, a prickling of intense attraction, then, as her eyes flicked to Jenny, a sudden rush of envy that Jenny should have such a superb secret lover.

'I'm sorry!' Rachel said into the silence. 'I didn't realise you had company. . .' She turned to shoo Tony out.

'Rachel, it's Damian Flint!' Tony whispered rapidly.

'He's here to see you!' Jenny moved forward. They spoke at the same time.

Rachel froze in the doorway. Then she spun, staring back at that hard-faced, powerful man, and felt her heart beat with abrupt violence.

'Damian Flint. . .?' Her voice was breathless with shock.

He stepped forward, said in a deep, smoky voice, 'Miss Swift, I'm afraid I have bad news for you. May we speak privately?'

Her heart stopped beating. 'My father. . .'

'Yes,' said Damian Flint. 'He's had a heart attack, a severe one, and he's in hospital. You must come home at once.'

The silence was momentary after he'd spoken. Rachel stood frozen, her face white and her eyes staring at his face as she pictured her father, felled by the pressure of his life and work, facing his arch-enemy: death. He had always been so afraid of death. For years, he had pitted himself against it, aware that it would mean the time for worrying about the future was over and the time for action had arrived.

'Poor Charles!' Tony said, appalled. 'When did this happen?'

'Tonight.' Damian Flint's mouth was hard as he studied Tony, blue eyes narrowed. 'I happened to be in London on business when my second-in-command rang to let me know the news. I came straight here.' He looked at Rachel, said curtly, 'Miss Swift, I must insist we speak privately.'

So there was more, she realised, staring at him, and suddenly knew that Jamie had had something to do with this. Her heart sank. She turned to Tony. 'You'd better go, darling. I'll see you when you get back to Hong Kong. It looks as if I'll be there before you.'

He bent his blond head, kissed her, and stroked her cheek. 'Take care, darling. Give my best wishes to your father.' He turned to leave.

'I'll see you to the door, Tony.' Jenny stepped forward, long red hair a blaze of colour against her translucent Celtic skin.

The door swung shut behind them. Alone with Damian Flint Rachel found him even more formidable than he had at first appeared. She felt tears sting at her eyes, and struggled to retain some self-control.

'The heart attack. . .' She moved to the table, put her keys down, suddenly realising she had been clutching them tightly. 'Where was he when it happened?'

'At home, in bed.' He studied her with hooded blue eyes. 'But this is where it gets tricky. Won't you sit down, Miss Swift? What I have to say might upset you even more than your father's heart attack.'

Paling, she sank into a green armchair, her eyes fixed on his hard-boned face. 'My uncle had something to do with it. . .'

'I'm afraid there was quite a scene last night in Hong Kong.' He walked coolly forward, hands thrust in black trouser pockets, jacket pushed back, the glitter of the watch-chain across that tight waistcoat almost hypnotic.

Rachel swallowed. 'Go on.'

'Your father had a dinner party for some very wealthy Japanese clients. Jamie arrived halfway through, uninvited. He was drunk. He started shouting insults at your father.'

She winced, closing her eyes, not wanting to hear what came next, because she could guess, knowing Jamie so well—his envy and hatred of her father, his lifelong ambitions thwarted again and again, driving him to drink and gambling and unreasoning rage.

'Your father tried to throw him out,' the hard voice said. 'A scuffle broke out. It continued into the court-yard where it turned into a fight. I understand it was quite ugly.'

'Was either of them hurt?' she asked thickly.

'Jamie got away with a black eye. Charles, however, sustained two broken ribs and a fractured jaw.'

'Oh, my God!' The words flew hoarsely from her lips as she got to her feet, hands at her mouth.

'Jamie's currently under arrest for assault,' said Damian Flint in a cool, hard voice. 'Charles was up for most of the night. First being patched up in hospital, then giving statements to the police, having Jamie arrested. . .he got home at six o'clock in the morning Hong Kong time and had the heart attack.'

Rachel swallowed, trembling. 'Was he alone?'

'No,' he said, watching her face. 'Luckily, the amah was awake and rang an ambulance on the spot. Quick-thinking girl. She also rang my second-in-command, who then rang me.'

'I must leave at once!' she whispered, and tried to move to the door. 'Book my flight, pack. . .'

Damian Flint blocked her path with his powerful chest. 'I've already taken care of your flight. We leave on the seven o'clock Cathay Direct to Hong Kong this morning.'

Her green eyes stared into his tough, handsome face. A *frisson* of alarmed awareness shot through her. Her eyes dropped of their own accord to his hard mouth.

Confused, she turned away. 'I'll go and pack.'

'It's three-thirty a.m.,' his dark voice called her back. 'We'll have to leave by four to make that flight.'

Rachel nodded, her hand on the doorknob. 'I'll be quick.' Then she let the door swing shut and went into her bedroom, feeling the tears sting her eyes like hot needles, her mouth trembling as she moved to her wardrobe, got her case, unzipped it and began blindly packing everything she could fit inside.

The lifelong feud between Jamie and Charles had turned into open warfare, then. Leaving Hong Kong had not just removed her from the battlefield; it had left them alone in it together for the first time in their lives.

There had always been someone else around to stop them. First her grandfather, Edward Swift. Although his two sons had hated each other, they would not have

dared move openly against one another while their
powerful father was still alive. Edward Swift had
founded Swift Investments, and left it to his eldest son,
Charles. Jamie — younger by ten years — had felt angry,
left out, dispossessed. Edward loved his youngest son,
and therefore had a clause written into his will, stating
that Swift Investments was to remain in the Swift
family. Charles had to sign a legal document testifying
to that effect the day he inherited. If he had no heirs,
the company would pass automatically to Jamie. He
had made this clause to ensure Jamie did not find
himself in Charles's power as he grew up. But, on the
contrary, it had been the beginning of the lifelong fight
for Swift, because Jamie knew it might one day fall
into his lap.

Twenty-five years ago, Charles had married
Marguerite, a beautiful French dancer, and Jamie had
been frantic, terrified of a powerful heir. When Rachel
was born, he'd relaxed a little. Rachel was female, and
therefore not as serious a threat as a son. Charles's
next child was born dead — a son. Then Marguerite
drowned in a boating accident just off Lantau Island,
and Charles was devastated. He had not married for
heirs; he had married for love. He never remarried,
never even looked at another woman, and the fight
started up again between the two men.

As Rachel grew up, the only heiress to this vast
fortune, she had blindly fallen into the battlefield
between the two men, loving both of them, truly
believing she could be the peacemaker.

It had taken twenty-two years of hell to realise that
their war was nothing to do with her, and that peace-
makers got torn to pieces. Jenny helped her see that.
Sensitive, intelligent, perceptive Jenny, who listened to
Rachel night after night as she cried and talked of

bringing peace, and said, 'You must save yourself, Rachel. You must stop participating in their war.' Eventually the words sank in, and when Jenny left Hong Kong, quietly dignified after rejection from Jamie, Rachel went with her.

She had lived in this flat for two years now, working as a secretary in the City, recovering from her life as a war victim, wanting only peace and freedom from her jealous, possessive father and her jealous, possessive uncle.

There was a knock at her door.

'Are you all right?' Jenny came in, green eyes deeply concerned.

'I'll cope.' Rachel shrugged, her voice husky.

'I'd fly back with you,' Jenny admitted, 'if I thought it would help. But it wouldn't, would it? That war is still going on, Jamie is still wasting his life on a childhood hatred and Edward Swift is still playing them off against each other from beyond the grave.'

Rachel studied her face, so pale and fine-boned, a light sprinkling of freckles on her nose. 'You knew it would happen, didn't you?' she said quietly. 'I remember you predicted it before I even left.'

Jenny nodded. 'Their final clash was always going to end in tragedy. I didn't want you to be caught in the crossfire when it came. Charles will have to make his move, now. He'll have to find a way round that clause in Edward's will.'

'Tony thinks it'll be Damian Flint. . .' Rachel said suddenly, remembering that conversation earlier tonight.

'The man in the living-room?' Jenny's lashes flickered and a smile touched her coral mouth. 'Yes, he looks like chairman material, doesn't he?'

'Very much so.' Rachel was frowning. 'Jamie

obviously agrees, or he wouldn't have written so many anti-Damian Flint letters to me!'

'But he's not family,' Jenny said quietly. 'Charles will have to leave everything to you, Rachel.'

She grimaced, zipped up her case. 'I'm no chairwoman. I'm a secretary to pay the rent, and a very lazy ex-ballerina with no ambitions other than to have a happy life and be free. My father may leave everything to me, but I frankly wouldn't know what to do with it other than give it to Jamie.'

'And he'd ruin it,' Jenny pointed out with a sigh. 'He's fatally flawed in that respect, Rachel.'

'It's insoluble,' Rachel agreed.

There was a little silence. Jenny was looking at her thoughtfully.

'I'm very impressed with Damian Flint,' she said suddenly. 'What do you think of him?'

Rachel prickled, thinking of the hard blue eyes, the uncompromising mouth and the cut of that black Savile Row suit, the effortless way he wore an invisible but formidable air of power.

'I don't like him!' she said with sudden feeling. 'He has a look of brutal ambition that I've always detested!'

'He's very sexy,' said Jenny with a smile. 'I caught my breath when I opened the door and found him towering over me.'

'Did he make a pass at you, then?' she asked teasingly, but there was a flash of envy and anger in her voice that she did not like or understand.

'No such luck!' laughed Jenny. 'He's been here for hours, though. He made a very exciting companion for the evening!'

Rachel felt the envy and anger again and was confused. 'Well, I've got to fly to Hong Kong with him! Thirteen hours on a jet!' She moved to the door with

her suitcase, opened the door, laughing. 'If I found Mr
Flint as exciting as you do, it would be all right. But as
it is I don't find him remotely attractive!'

She turned and walked straight into Damian Flint's
hard chest.

Looking up with a gasp, she saw him watching her
with narrowed blue eyes, his mouth a hard line. He
had heard what she'd said and he didn't like it.

'Ready, Miss Swift?' he asked tightly.

Hot colour burned her cheeks. 'Yes. . .yes, of
course!' Flustered, she handed him her case and he
took it with a strong hand, his face hard.

'Good luck!' Jenny saw them to the door, kissed
Rachel. 'Give your father my love. And. . . Jamie too.'

'I'll especially give your love to Jamie,' Rachel said
with an understanding smile. 'God knows, he needs it
now.'

'Goodbye, Mr Flint.' Jenny extended a pale, slender
hand. 'I'm glad we met. And I'll remember what you
said about love.'

Rachel tensed, did a double-take.

'What was it again?' Jenny said. 'You said you'd
read it somewhere. That love was. . .'

'An erotic expression of the soul through the body!'
drawled Damian Flint with a sardonic smile, and bent
his dark head to kiss Jenny's hand. 'Goodbye, Jenny.
Thank you for such interesting company!'

Listening to this astonishing exchange, Rachel more
than prickled.

She felt angry, insignificant, and envious of her
friend's Celtic beauty for the first time.

They went downstairs in silence. Damian Flint strode
out into the cool night air. Of course, the Rolls-Royce
limousine was his, and he rapped sharply on the
window to waken the sleeping chauffeur.

As they drove to the airport, Rachel said, 'So. . .
why were you discussing love with my flatmate?'

'Just one of those late-night conversations,' he
drawled, watching her in the darkened interior as the
car shot along the motorway.

'You were with her for around five hours, weren't
you?' She was smiling, but for some reason her smile
was tight. 'How did you get on to the subject of love?'

The blue eyes flicked away from her. 'We just did.'

Rachel felt summarily dismissed and was angry.
Looking out at the dark motorway strip, she decided
she hated Damian Flint. He had obviously found Jenny
attractive. Had he made a pass at her? Had they
kissed? The thoughts flashed through her mind uncon-
trolled. They aroused anger and she felt uncomfortable
with it, shifting, frowning.

'That was young Tony Radcliffe you were out with,
wasn't it?'

Rachel turned her head, surprised by the dark, cool
voice. 'Yes. . .'

'Known him long?' he asked, but his face was
expressionless and she knew he was only making polite
conversation.

Flippantly, she said, 'We're childhood sweethearts.'

The blue eyes moved over her slender body in the
red dress. 'It must be difficult to sustain a romance at
such a distance. Does he come to London to see you
regularly?'

'We keep in close touch,' she replied shortly, deliberately trying to mimic his earlier dismissal by turning
her face away as she spoke.

They drove on in silence. Rachel was deeply aware
of him in the luxurious rear of the limousine beside
her. His hard thighs brushed hers as he shifted suddenly, picking up the telephone nestling in the armrest.

Rachel jumped as though burnt, turning to stare down at his hard thigh, then saw the phone in his hand, her eyes shooting to his through her lashes. 'Not ringing the airport? I thought you said you'd booked our flight!'

'I'm calling a friend who happened to be in London with me,' he drawled coolly. 'She'll ring Hong Kong, let them know we're on our way.'

Rachel nodded and looked away. She suddenly remembered Tony saying, 'Women fall at his feet, power falls into his lap, and money grows on the palm trees in his back garden. . .'

'Domino?' His voice grew smoky, seductive. 'Yes . . .she's with me now, we're on our way to Heathrow . . .would you? Thanks. Yes. . .when you get back.' He laughed softly. 'Sounds just what I need!'

Rachel listened to this very obvious conversation in tense silence, prickling with an increasing dislike for Damian Flint. She wondered who this Domino was and what she looked like. Obviously, the woman was his mistress.

When he'd put the phone down, Rachel asked. 'Who will this woman ring? My father or my uncle?'

'Your father,' he said flatly, eyes narrowing.

Her eyes lit with hope. 'You mean he's well enough to take a call? I thought you said——'

'Your father is keen to have you back,' he cut in. 'The hospital asked me to let them know as soon as you were on your way. They think it might speed his recovery. He's missed you very badly.'

Guilt flooded her in waves and she put a hand to her temple. 'He never mentioned it to me. . .never gave any indication. . .'

'He knew you wanted to be independent,' Damian Flint said coolly. 'But this attack has hit him hard

enough to call you back at once. It's been building up
for some time, I think.'

Alarmed, she said, 'You talk as though he
could——'

'Die?' The blue eyes flicked to her, ruthlessness in
their depths. 'We all have to do that sooner or later,
Miss Swift. The problem is that Charles is being harried
into an early grave by the burden he's unable to set
down.'

Rachel met his gaze, then gave a jerky nod and
looked away. If only my little brother hadn't been born
dead, she thought. If only my mother hadn't died. If
only I were capable of taking over Swift myself, but
I'm not, I never was, I never will be—I just couldn't
face it, all the pressure, the ruthless cut-throat ambition
of everyone trying to stab me in the back and take my
place. . .

'There is a solution to the pressure he's under, of
course,' said the man beside her. 'It's just going to take
a little time to put into operation. But time is now the
one thing your father hasn't got.'

Rachel looked at him sharply. 'What solution? Tell
me!'

The black lashes flickered as he said, 'I'm sure your
father will discuss it with you at the appropriate
moment. . .'

He looked away again, dismissing her. He was good
at that, she thought, her dislike for him intensifying.
No wonder Jamie feared him—having met him, she
could see why. All those letters from her uncle, ranting
incessantly on the subject of Damian Flint, how he had
walked into a senior position in Swift and was poised
to take the whole company from under Jamie's nose.
Rachel racked her brains, trying to remember what
Jamie had said of him—ruthless, living only for his

ambition. She had not listened when he spoke of Flint. She had assumed his letters were the product of his lifelong rage, the festering cancer of his childhood, driving him into unreasonable behaviour, and a tendency to see the worst in anyone who was a friend of Charles.

But he had obviously been right about Damian Flint.

They arrived at the airport, and were rushed on to the 747 to Hong Kong. The engines whined softly as beautiful Oriental stewardesses showed them to their seats in First Class and offered them complimentary champagne, which they both refused.

'What will happen to Jamie?' Rachel asked as the jet roared into take-off, leaving London behind them in a blue-grey dawn. 'You say he's been charged with assault. . .'

'That's something else you'll have to ask your father,' Damian Flint drawled coolly beside her.

'But if the charge of assult goes through——'

'He might end up in prison. Quite.' He flicked narrowed eyes at her. 'I imagine your father will eventually drop the charges. But only once he's well enough to consider dealing with his brother.'

Rachel gave a shaky sigh. 'Poor Jamie. . .!' If only, she thought, there was a way to help him come to terms with the rage that had coloured his whole life.

'Perhaps you should try to sleep,' Damian Flint said coolly. 'You've already been up all night. Sitting up worrying about your "beloved" uncle won't help!'

Rachel's eyes flashed at the tone of his voice, particularly the way he said 'beloved' with a sting, a subtle edge of sarcasm and a look of hard distaste on his face.

'I love my father and my uncle—equally,' she said tightly.

'Did I pass comment?' he drawled, brows lifting sardonically.

'I felt you did!' she said tightly.

A hard smile twisted his mouth. 'Miss Swift, I can assure you it was your imagination.'

She smiled back, her eyes angry. 'I don't think so.'

There was a little silence.

'I see,' he drawled. 'Well, let's not argue about it. This is neither the time nor the ——'

'I think it is,' she said suddenly, and her heart beat fast as she felt the hatred burn in her eyes, directly at him, her mouth a tight line, her body rigid with anger.

'Miss Swift,' he said slowly, eyes narrowing, 'you're tired, you've had a bad shock and——'

'And I'm hysterical?'

'I didn't say that,' he murmured, but he was no longer smiling or trying to pacify her.

'It's what you thought, though,' she said tightly. 'And I'd like to find out what else you think, Mr Damian Flint, on our thirteen-hour flight to Hong Kong!'

CHAPTER TWO

THE jet flew upwards, pushing through white clouds, and the sun blazed gold across that ethereal skyscape. Light shone full on Damian's face, sharpening it, enhancing the tough angularity of his cheekbones, the winged black brows above glittering blue eyes fringed by black lashes, and the cool, ruthless line of his mouth. His lean and powerful body was relaxed in the black suit, long legs crossed towards her, chest turned towards her, and he was watching her with narrowed eyes, obviously rearranging his thoughts about her at a rate of knots.

'OK, Miss Swift,' he said softly, 'shoot from the hip.'

Her lashes flickered. She paused, unnerved by the way he spoke and the words he chose. But her anger and dislike were getting the better of her, and she wanted very much to have an argument with him — and win it.

'You don't like Jamie very much,' she said as an opening gambit, 'do you?'

His eyes glittered. 'What makes you think that?'

Rachel smiled. 'I'm in close touch with my uncle. He keeps me informed.' Her pulses leapt a little as she realised he was amused by her decision to confront him. That meant he didn't take her anger seriously, thought he could beat her hands down, and that surely gave her the advantage?

'And what exactly,' he drawled with a hard smile, 'has your uncle told you about me?'

Rachel smiled like a green-eyed cat. 'Well, now, let

me see. He's told me that you're now senior partner of
Far East Swift. . .'

'True,' he said coolly. 'What of it?'

'Well. . .it makes you very powerful within the
company.'

The blue eyes were narrowed. 'I enjoy power. Some
people don't. I enjoy the work, too, and I handle my
. . .power, Miss Swift, with care.'

'I'm sure you handle it with forensic skill.'

He laughed softly, but his eyes glittered as he saw
the hatred in hers. 'Why, thank you! I'm flattered.'

'Ambitious people always enjoy power,' Rachel
countered at once. 'And that's another thing I've been
told about you: that you're very ambitious.'

'I'd go along with that,' he drawled non-committally.

She smiled. 'Jamie says you're ruthless when it comes
to getting what you want.'

'Jamie could be right,' he said softly, his hard-boned
face devastatingly handsome. 'But then we're all driven
by our own demons, aren't we? Even Jamie.'

'And what,' she asked softly, 'would your demons
be, Mr Flint?'

The blue eyes mocked her. 'Well, it's like this, you
see,' he murmured. 'I had a tough childhood and it
spurred me on to great heights.'

Her pulses were very fast. 'A sad story. Forgive me
if I don't burst into tears, but the great heights seem
more than compensatory.'

He laughed again, flicking blue eyes to her face.
'Yes, I think so too!'

'Jamie,' she said, 'told me a little about your ultimate
ambitions.'

He was leaning very close to her, a hard smile on his
ruthless mouth, amused by her hostility and cleverly
phrased attack on his very ruthless character.

'Shall I regale you with my uncle's suspicions about you?' Rachel asked.

'Oh, I'm all ears, Miss Swift!' he drawled with a cool gesture from one strong tanned hand before replacing it below his hard jaw.

'Well,' she said softly, 'he said that you want to take over Swift Investments, disinherit him, marry the perfect wife and found a dynasty.'

'Is that what he said?' Damian Flint murmured with a glint of mockery behind his hooded eyelids.

'Oh, yes, he did,' purred Rachel. 'And he also said you wanted to do all that before you were thirty-five. How old are you now, Mr Flint?'

The cynical mouth murmured, 'Thirty-three. . .'

'Only two years before D-Day?' Her green eyes mocked him. 'Tut, tut, Mr Flint. You surely haven't miscalculated?'

'Oh, not me.' The blue eyes flicked up to meet hers, deadly, mocking, completely self-assured. 'I never miscalculate.'

She felt breathless. 'But how clever! Do tell me how you're going to do it! I simply must know your game plan! After all, you'll have to move pretty fast to do all that in two years, won't you?'

'Oh, I think I'll make it,' he said softly. 'After all, I only have to make the right moves at the right time.'

'You'll have to grab opportunities left, right and centre.'

'I'm an old hand at that.'

She smiled tensely. 'I'm sure you are. But those opportunities might not be yours. They might belong to somebody else. How will you grab them then?'

He leaned closer. 'I'll tell you a little secret,' he said softly. 'Opportunities belong to the people who take them.'

'Is that so?' she said, heart thudding.

'Oh, yes,' he murmured, and he was no longer smiling. 'The world we live in, you see, is only a step from the jungle. There are predators. . .and there are prey. Predators are the ones who take opportunities, and prey. . .well, they just get torn to pieces, Miss Swift. Left in the sun for the vultures to feed on.' His eyes glinted at her. 'Sad but true. What a dangerous world. No blessings for the meek and everybody shakes when a predator begins to hunt.' One long finger touched her naked throat, making her shiver. 'I wonder . . .which are you, Miss Swift? Predator or prey?'

She stared at his ruthless face and felt afraid.

'I know which I am,' he confided softly. 'Because everybody shakes when I walk past. It used to upset me — really, you have no idea. But now I just think of those vultures and carry on my predatory way. . .'

Rachel was almost shaking herself, studying his face, listening to his softly spoken words, and her heart was pounding fiercely; she felt fear and excitement flooding her and she knew she could not match him — not tonight, not with the strain she was under.

'An interesting conversation, Mr Flint,' she said tightly, 'but I'm afraid my eyelids are beginning to droop. I think I'll try to get some sleep.'

'Tired, Miss Swift?' he drawled mockingly. 'And I thought you wanted to talk all through the flight!'

'Exhaustion seems to have caught up with me!'

He watched her, his face hard and his blue eyes glittering. 'You disappoint me,' he said under his breath, and Rachel's heart beat even faster at the darkness in his voice.

Breathless, she said tightly, 'Would you mind switching off the overhead light?'

'Not at all,' he murmured, and reached up a strong

hand to flick it out, but not before Rachel had noticed how long his fingers were, and how black hairs grew over his wrists and down towards those fingers.

Turning from him, she pulled her blanket up to her shoulders and tried to recline her seat, frowning as she hunted for the button.

'Let me do that. . .' Damian Flint said smoothly, and leant across her, his powerful chest pressing against her, his hard mouth inches from hers.

Heart pounding erratically, she stared into his eyes. 'It's quite all right, I ——'

The seat reclined back slowly, and he watched her, unsmiling, his blue eyes moving with deliberate sexual assessment over her body, his hand accidentally-on-purpose sliding the blanket from her.

Rachel shook visibly. She felt almost stripped, lying on her back, staring up at his hard face and powerful body. No man had ever looked at her like that in her life, and his eyes left her in no uncertain terms as to what he was thinking.

Alarmed, she fumbled with her right hand for her blanket, breathing erratically, staring up at him as he loomed over her.

'What are you looking for?' Damian Flint said softly, his mouth inches from hers. 'Your blanket? It's a little too late to go undercover now — don't you think?'

Her face went scarlet and she just stared at him, green eyes wide with the realisation of just how danger-ous he was.

'But here.' He picked up her blanket, spread it over her trembling body, his long fingers brushing her naked throat as she quivered angrily and snatched at the blanket, glaring at him. 'Let me tuck you in and bid you goodnight. You're going to need all the rest you can get!'

'Thank you so much!' she said in a furious voice. 'Goodnight!'

As she turned her back on him, she was breathless with rage, lying staring at the darkened wall of the cabin, aware he had completely turned her confrontation to his advantage and beaten her hands down.

No wonder Jamie feared Damian Flint. My God, she thought, closing her eyes tightly, I fear him too. Then she told herself he had only got the better of her because she was, as he had so rightly said, suffering from shock and exhaustion.

Rachel's head began to ache and throb. Hot tears filled her eyes and she did not fight them, her face hidden by the darkness in the cabin. Thank God her father had survived, but for how many more years could he go on, with only Rachel to inherit while Jamie hung around in the background, desperate to take the firm, simply to settle a childhood score?

It occurred to her that the depths of her pain were tinged by guilt. Stale news. She knew all about her guilt. She had colossal reserves of it, absolutely huge, cut into her by her father — begging her from childhood to hate Jamie. By Jamie — begging her from childhood to hate her father. Guilt and more guilt. Guilt because she had run from them. Guilt because she had not been there to stop Jamie losing control. Guilt because she had not been at her father's side when death had sent him this violent warning.

Exhausted from her tears, Rachel fell asleep, and the jet flew on across time-zones, across the Middle East, across a blood-red sky.

It was a restless sleep. Though the huge armchair reclined almost full-length, it still was not a bed. Rachel twisted and turned in her sleep, waking occasionally to hear the constant throb of the aircraft engines, then falling asleep again.

The stewardesses woke them for a champagne breakfast. Rachel went to the bathroom, washed at the metal sink, and brushed out her long black curly hair. She felt wretched.

Still the flight went on. Daylight streamed through the aircraft windows. Rachel sat in tense silence beside the detestable Damian Flint. She wasn't going to risk being thrashed again in conversation, not yet, not until she'd had a chance to recharge her worn batteries.

So they sat in tense silence together, reading. He was reading a book on political and economic history. She made a face at it, and buried her nose in a bestseller all about powerful families. Then the father in the book had a fatal heart attack and she went white, putting it down, tears burning her eyes as the aircraft engines whined on and on, and the Oriental stewardesses moved gracefully around the cabin, collecting drinks and trays.

'We're here,' Damian said suddenly beside her, and closed his book.

Rachel sat up as the announcement crackled over the tannoy. They were in descent, sliding down through clouds, and she peered out intently, her heart beating, waiting for a glimpse of the colony.

There it was, white skyscrapers gleaming in the sparkling dawn, the blue harbour waters dappled with gold, ships in that fragrant harbour between the Kowloon Peninsula and the gorse-dotted hills of the island.

'When can I see my father?' she demanded, still staring out at the city she had been born in, and feeling waves of love for its brash life force, its moneyed pavements and its frantic race against time.

'This morning,' he said coolly. 'I'll drive you there myself.'

'That won't be necessary. I'll get a taxi.' She turned, gave him a tight, hostile smile. 'My father's villa is in Repulse Bay, quite a drive from the city. I wouldn't want to put you to any trouble.'

'No trouble at all,' he drawled. 'I own the villa next door to him.'

There was a stunned silence. Her eyes met his, saw the lazy mockery in their depths, and she felt her heart racing faster, realising anew how very dangerous he was to her family.

When she thought her voice would remain steady, she said, 'Next door?'

'Mmm. Right next door.' A hard smile touched his mouth. 'Why, Miss Swift, you've gone quite white. Nothing wrong, I hope?'

'Nothing at all,' she said tightly. Turning her head to look out of the window again, she felt her heart drumming with rage. The villa next door!

The aircraft swooped in to land, almost touching the little buildings of Kowloon. Kai Tak stretched ahead, runway strip in the harbour lit up in blue white and gold, and a second later they had cleared the buildings of the city and were landing with a faint jolt.

'A car is meeting us,' Damian told her as they disembarked.

'Oh, good.' Rachel walked behind him, dishevelled, weary and full of resentment that Damian Flint should look as cool and immaculate as he had when he'd first arrived.

As they left the building, waves of moist humid air wrapped around her skin. The car—a white Mercedes—was chauffeur-driven and, thankfully, air-conditioned. It sped through the streets of Tsimshatsui, then up through the tunnel to Hong Kong island itself. Rachel barely glanced at the familiar streets. She was too busy coming to terms with the fact that she was back, she was home, after two years of freedom in London. Then they were on the cliff road for Repulse Bay, and the sea glittered below her to the right.

The car drove in through the dusty, bleached stone gates to the stone courtyard where a fountain played and cicadas buzzed noisily in the palms and jacarandas moved softly in the hot sea air.

Damian helped her from the Mercedes. 'I'll get your case.'

The front door of the villa opened. A beautiful Chinese woman stepped out, smart in white cheongsam slit to the thighs, her eyes dark and sparkly.

Rachel smiled at her and said, 'Hello, Nightingale.'

'Miss Rachel!' Nightingale walked with quick, light steps towards her and her smile was radiant. 'Oh, such trouble since you been gone!'

Rachel embraced her. 'Any news from the hospital?'

'Same thing. Mr Charles, he doing fine, he better very soon.'

'Let's hope they're right,' Rachel said. Nightingale had been her father's amah for five years, and was younger than Rachel, but was hard-working and loyal, kept the villa as clean as a new pin, and was becoming a part of the family.

Damian Flint loomed beside them with Rachel's case. 'I'll leave you to unpack, rest and change. Visiting hours start at eleven. I'll pick you up at ten-thirty.'

'I'll be ready for you,' Rachel said tightly, her eyes hostile as she looked at him through black lashes.

'Will you, Miss Swift?' he murmured sardonically, and studied her full red mouth. 'I'll be sure to brush up my fencing skills, then. . .just for you!'

He deposited her case at the front door then strode
back to his car, and she watched him go with hatred,
her eyes moving over his powerful body, so lean, so
tall, so impeccably dressed. He got in and the car
pulled away.

'Mr Damian,' Nightingale sighed in the heat beside
her, 'he so sexy!'

'I'm afraid I can't see it,' snapped Rachel, and turned
to walk into the cool air-conditioned stone hallway of
the villa.

'Every woman want him!' Nightingale followed her.

'I'm not every woman!' Rachel moved towards the
stairs, trying to ignore Nightingale's adoration of the
detestable Mr Flint.

'Mr Charles, he say, "Damian Flint is son I never
had."'

Rachel froze on the bottom stair, heart stopping,
and her head turned slowly to look at the pretty amah.
'My father said that?'

'Every day since you gone.'

'That Damian Flint is the son he never had?'

'Sure thing.'

Rachel was silent for a long moment, her face pale.
Damian Flint was obviously picking up chairman-of-
the-board points at a rate that defied imagination.

Dismissing him with difficulty from her mind, she
went to her bedroom, smiling at the familiar old room,
the shutters flung wide, overlooking the dusty terrace
below, the bright pink bougainvillaea trailing like a
Schiaparelli ballgown from the bleached balustrade
walls below, down the rugged red cliffs, down to that
turqouise, glittering sea.

Switching the fan overhead to full speed, Rachel
unpacked, put everything in her heated wardrobe. It
was early July, the heat was moist, and her clothes

would grow mould if the wardrobe wasn't heated. Then she took a shower and changed into a cool sundress. When Damian Flint arrived to pick her up, she was more than ready for him.

He had showered too, his black hair faintly damp on his white shirt collar, and now he wore a different suit, impeccably cut in finest grey cloth, a silver watch-chain across his formal waistcoat, silver cuff-links gleaming at hair-roughened wrists, every inch the chairman of the board.

'My, my, you do look ready for me!' he drawled softly, his blue gaze roving with deliberate sexual insolence over her slender curves.

Rachel flushed angrily. 'Thank you, Mr Flint! Shall we go?' She moved past his powerful, lean body, prickling with awareness, and walked into the sunlight.

'Do you feel settled in?' he asked with cool, polite mockery, striding with her in the hot, humid morning towards the white Mercedes parked by the courtyard fountain.

'Oh, very much so,' Rachel said sweetly, hating him as he towered over her, opening the rear door of the car for her. 'I'm so used to the long-haul flights from Hong Kong to Europe. I can see you are, too.'

He gave her a glittering, sardonic look. 'Yes. . .how clever of you to notice! You see, I now handle all international affairs. I have done for some time.'

'Really?' Her green eyes gleamed with hatred. 'What an international man you are! Flying back and forth for Swift Investments. New York, London, Paris, Munich. . .?'

'Don't forget Japan,' he drawled softly.

Rachel's smile tightened. Lowering her lashes, she slid into the car. The air-conditiioning was cool on her face. Damian got in beside her, making her deeply

aware of his hard body. The chauffeur pulled away
slowly, rounding the fountain in the circular drive,
edging through the gates tentatively. A sky-blue bus
lumbered past, then they shot out on to the curving
mountain road behind it, and a second later overtook
it with a roar that must have terrified the already
nervous passengers, as the buses always drove mania-
cally around these bends, desperate to stick to their
schedule right down to the last fraction of a second.

'I had a very interesting chat with Nightingale,'
Rachel said softly as they shot along in the white
Mercedes. 'She told me that my father is very fond of
you.'

'I'm very fond of him.'

'She also said that my father sees you as the son he
never had.'

'How women gossip!' drawled Damian Flint.

'Everyone in Hong Kong gossips. Did you know
that? Yes, I'm sure you did. It's that kind of town, isn't
it? I simply can't wait to find out what other people
have to say. . .'

There was a brief silence. The sea was azure-blue to
their left, the cliffs dusty beige to their right. The
atmosphere pulsed with a subtle but distinct menace.

'You wouldn't be threatening me with Chinese whis-
pers, would you, Miss Swift?' he said softly, steel
edging his voice, 'I'd hate to think you were a scandalmonger. Especially about me.'

Her heart skipped beats. 'Of course not, Mr Flint!'

'I'm glad about that,' he said under his breath, eyes
suddenly very deadly indeed. 'Because if you were I
might be tempted to retaliate, and you wouldn't like
that. Things could get nasty.'

Breathless, she said, 'I meant I would no doubt hear

about you through the grapevine, Mr Flint, not that I would personally——'

'Of course not!' he drawled softly, menace in his voice. 'You wouldn't want to antagonise me any more than you already have. Would you. . . Miss Swift?'

Rachel was silent, watching him steadily, held in check by the menace in his hard face, her heart beating very hard indeed.

'Because,' said Damian Flint, 'when antagonism springs up between a man and a woman, it's really just a fight for supremacy. And there's only one way to end it.' His blue eyes dropped suddenly to probe the hollow between her breasts, watching them rise and fall. 'Do you understand me?'

'Oh, yes!' she said tightly, rage in her glittering eyes. 'You're saying plainly that you'll assert yourself in the most obvious way possible if I ever attempt to cross you!'

'Clever girl!' he said softly, and flicked his blue gaze directly to hers, sending a throb of excitement to her solar plexus. 'But then—it's an idle threat, isn't it? Because I'm sure you won't try to cross me from now on. Will you?'

Her body was alive, throbbing with pulses she never knew she had, and as she jerked her face away from his she knew he had once again defeated her, outclassed her, and she knew without a doubt that he was right: if there was ever a real fight between her and Damian Flint, he would take supremacy, she would be overpowered by the fierce excitement burning in her now, and he would walk away with victory on a scale she did not dare imagine.

They sped onwards, down from Repulse Bay, then up the steep, winding mountain roads to the peak, the old walls of mid-levels giving a view straight down into

Central District, the heart of money and power in
Hong Kong, its white skyscrapers shrouded in faint
sunlit mist and the shimmer of humid heat.

Soon they were driving into the hospital car park.

'Your father's expecting us,' Damian Flint drawled
as he got out of the Mercedes. 'But although he may
seem quite well he's still to be handled with care. Don't
do or say anything that might upset him.'

'You hardly need to tell me that,' she snapped,
hating him.

Following Damian inside, she shivered at the anti-
septic smell of the neat white corridors, the nurses
talking in hushed voices, the squeak of rubber-soled
shoes, the clatter of a trolley, and the enigmatic faces
of doctors in white coats who walked past them every
now and then.

The doctor was walking with them towards the
private rooms. 'But you'd better not see him for too
long. Five or ten minutes at the most. I don't want him
to get excited or upset.'

They were taken to a room with walls of glass,
overlooked by a central console with nurses in
attendance.

'Visitors for you, Mr Swift,' the doctor said, opening
the door, and Charles Swift looked up with a bright
smile.

'Rachel!' He held out his arms to her.

'Hello, Father!' Rachel said huskily, walking to his
bedside and trying not to be alarmed by his appearance
as she hugged and kissed him.

He looked as though he had aged about twenty
years. His ribs were bandaged, his jaw in traction, and
wires were stuck in his wrists and chest to register his
hearbeat on a sinister machine behind him that flashed
his beats per minute in red digits.

'Rachel. . .thank God you're home!' Charles took
her hand and clung to it. 'Damian brought you back to
me. I knew he would. Knew he'd understand immediately that it was time. . .'

'Try not to talk too much.' Damian stepped forward.
'You should be resting.'

'I can do that now,' Charles said in a thready voice.
'Can't I, Damian? Now that you're in charge, now that
you've brought her home. . .'

Rachel frowned, shooting a glance at Damian. Now
that he was in charge and had brought her home? What
was being said—or rather, what was not being said?

Charles groped for Damian's hand suddenly. 'I can
always rely on you, can't I, Damian?'

'Always,' Damian replied in that deep, cool voice,
and in that moment Rachel saw how close the bond
between the two men was, how much Charles relied on
Damian, and how deeply aware of that reliance
Damian was. It both touched and appalled her.
Damian had made it clear he was acting only out of
ambition. Surely the situation could only end in
betrayal?

Charles looked back at Rachel. 'You will stay, won't
you? For good, I mean. Make Hong Kong your home
again, not London, too far away. . .'

Outside the window, the waters of the harbour
gleamed azure-blue, and Lantau Island loomed out of
a faint mist. Green, lush, mysterious, it reminded her
of her mother, Marguerite, and the tragic way she had
died off those deserted shores of Lantau. A deep ache
tugged at her, tears stung her eyes, she looked back at
her father.

'Of course I'll stay,' she said. 'I'll never leave you
again.' And she meant it, every word.

Charles gave a hoarse sigh and relaxed. 'Thank God! But if you stay you need a job. . . Damian — is there a post vacant at Swift?'

'My secretary,' Damian Flint said flatly, and her eyes shot to his face.

'I don't want to be your secretary!' she said in a voice choked with rage and hostility.

His eyes narrowed. 'I need a secretary; you need a job. Take it.'

'No!'

'But why?' Charles asked, appalled. 'You should take the job. It's the only way to make sure ——' The heart machine behind him bleeped noisily as his heart-beat shot up dramatically.

'Lie back, Father!' she urged, alarmed by the flashing digits on the heart machine.

'Take the job,' Damian Flint said under his breath.

She stared at him. 'But ——'

'Rachel, please!' Charles was clinging to her hand.

'I'm afraid I must ask you to leave now!' The doctor had opened the door suddenly, was walking in with two nurses, directing them to either side of the bed as the heart machine flashed and beeped alarmingly.

'What's happening?' Rachel was on her feet. 'Is it another attack?'

'Take the job!' Damian bit out under his breath, standing too.

Charles clung to her hand. 'I want you to work with him. Get to know him. He's a good man, a strong man; he can save us all!'

'I'll take the job!' she said automatically.

'You're hired!' Damian bit out, and took her by the wrist, dragging her to the door while the nurses began moving Charles, filling needles, checking his blood-pressure, tapping buttons on the heart machine.

'Damian is the one!' Charles called raggedly as they left. 'Listen to him, Rachel! Not Jamie! Not Jamie. . .'

Damian pulled her out and shut the door, marching with her back down the corridors, his hand hard on her wrist, and as she went with him, hurrying to match those long strides, she understood and was horrified beyond belief.

Charles planned to marry her off to this man. He planned it, and Damian Flint was going to see that it happened. Together, they were planning her marriage.

Never! she thought fiercely. Never as long as I live will I marry that sinister shark who pretends to be so smooth and loyal and hard-working. He may have my father fooled, but he doesn't fool me. Rage welled up in her as she thought of the way he had come to get her in London, so cool, so confident, so very self-assured.

Had Jamie not warned her from the beginning that he was dangerous, and that he wanted Swift Invest-ments to further his massive ambitions, she would have responded to his sex appeal, his hard good looks, his cool, clever wit.

Even Jenny—clever, perceptive Jenny—had been impressed by Damian Flint, had found him apparently irresistible, staying up till early morning with him, discussing love; and how that galled her, how it angered her.

Shooting a fierce look of hatred at Damian Flint beside her, striding along, his face hard, she saw a ruthless swine whose main objective was to get Rachel to be his wife so he could fulfil his ambitions and take Swift for his own. Think again, my friend, she seethed inside. Think again!

As they left the hospital, she said tightly to Damian, 'Any word from my uncle?'

'Ah. . .the beloved Jamie!' drawled Damian, striding beside her into the sunlight, the humidity, the dusty bleached colonial landscape of the peak. 'I wondered when his name would crop up again!'

'He's my uncle and I love him,' Rachel said with a tight smile, heart drumming with rage. 'I take it he's still living in Tai Hang Road?'

Damian opened the door of the white Mercedes, surveyed her with narrowed eyes. 'Naturally.'

'Is he at work this week?' She kept her lashes lowered to hide the raging green fire of her eyes.

'No, he's been suspended, given the circumstances.'

'I'll telephone him as soon as I get home,' Rachel said under her breath, and slid into the car.

Damian slid in beside her, closed the door. The chauffeur pulled away, past colonial buildings, flagpoles with Union Jacks fluttering, green lawns and fountains and shimmering humidity.

'What about the assault charges?' Rachel asked. 'Obviously I can't bother my father with them yet. But something must be done.'

'Don't trouble yourself. Leave it to me. I can handle it.'

'I'll thank you, Mr Flint,' she snapped, 'to leave me to deal with my family relationships as I see fit!'

There was a tense silence. A menacing glitter entered Damian's eyes.

'As you wish,' he drawled, and his voice was pure steel. 'In the meantime, I'll expect you at the office on Monday morning. That gives you three days to acclimatise. Shall we say—nine o'clock sharp?'

'Nine o'clock sharp,' she agreed through her teeth, and as she turned her head their eyes locked and she felt afraid, very afraid, because she knew he was stronger.

CHAPTER THREE

'I WAS right, then.' Jamie was as appalled as she had known he would be, his blue eyes glittering with hatred as he spoke through his teeth. 'Flint is going to take it all — the Hong Kong office, the international network, the whole damned thing.'

She had telephoned him as soon as she got home, and he'd come straight to the villa, arriving in a whirlwind, his personality magnetic as always. Charisma was the one thing Jamie had never been short of. He looked older, though his hair was still black. But there were sprinklings of silver at this temples, and his hard-boned face was more lined. He was six feet two, and wore dark blue trousers with a blue and white striped shirt. Drinking had put weight on him; his stomach protruded slightly.

Rachel said under her breath, 'I won't marry him, Jamie!'

He watched her intently, suspicion in his eyes.

'I mean it!' She turned, studying him across the living-room, the polished wood floor gleaming, the fan whirring overhead. 'No matter what he says or does, no matter what happens to force me towards him — I'd die rather than marry Damian Flint!'

'Thank God!' Jamie gave a hoarse sigh, moving to her, his arms going around her. 'Forgive me for being wary! But ever since you've gone they've been conspiring against me, plotting, and ——'

'Jamie, why did you cause that scene?' She pulled back to study him, tears in her eyes. 'To hit my father!

Your own brother, Jamie! If you could see him in hospital. . .the wires, the bandages, the ——'

'I was crazy that night,' he said thickly. 'So damned jealous of Flint, so full of hatred for Charles. I drank myself into oblivion. I don't even remember hitting Charles. All I remember is waking up in a prison cell with a colossal headache.'

She struggled to see both sides of the story, but it was hard, very hard, because although she felt compassion for Jamie she also felt anger: he had almost killed her father.

Jamie read her expression well, and pleaded with her, his hands on her shoulders. 'Rachel, I swear to you, I didn't know what I was doing!'

She drew a shaky breath, nodded, her face white. 'Have you. . .tried to see him in hospital?'

'They won't even let me into the building.' His mouth twisted bitterly. 'Flint, of course! He telephoned the hospital from London, left strict instructions not to let me see Charles.'

Rachel could see the reasoning behind that, but nevertheless felt angry towards Damian Flint — not because he had so obviously done the right thing, but because he was so clearly in complete control of a situation that had always been beyond Rachel.

'When do you start work for him?' Jamie asked suddenly.

'Monday morning,' she said huskily.

He nodded, eyes narrowing. 'Just make sure you're never alone with the bastard.'

She whitened, appalled. 'You don't think he'd try to ——'

'Seduce you?' Jamie's voice was grim. 'It's the smart move, Rachel. You're the key to his future.'

When Jamie had gone, Rachel sat alone on the

terrace in the hot sun and watched a gecko lizard flicker across the dusty stone. Nothing had changed, then. Not really. Charles was trying to keep her one hundred per cent on his side. Jamie was doing exactly the same. Rachel suddenly felt she'd been through an emotional wringer. The only part of her personal life in Hong Kong which was different was Damian Flint, and the threat he represented was so great she simply did not know how to deal with it.

A black hornet flew past, toyed with the bright pink flowers of the bougainvillaea. Rachel watched it, remembering Jamie's words. 'Seduce you? It's the smart move. . .' Her eyes flared with furious determination. Just let him try, she thought fiercely!

On Monday morning, she reported to work at the Swift building on Des Voeux Road. Central District was a fast-paced money-making centre, the streets littered with towering banks, finance giants and international hotels. Trams rattled, taxis blared their horns, and everywhere skyscrapers rose like jagged teeth to touch the azure sky.

She had dressed very carefully in a plain white cotton shift dress with scoop neckline, short sleeves, and flat silver sandals. Her long black hair was pulled back in a pony-tail.

As she got out of the lift on the top floor, Damian Flint came striding along the corridor and they collided.

'Oh. . .!' Rachel flushed, recoiling from his hard chest with angry awareness. 'Must you rush around without looking where you're going!'

'You got in *my* way,' Damian Flint said softly, his eyes narrowed. 'Not the other way round. Try not to make a habit of it. . .' His gaze dropped, watching the rise and fall of her breasts. 'Good choice of dress.

Efficient. . .but very sexy. Admirable taste, Miss Swift.
I shall enjoy watching you move around the office.'

Heat flared in her cheeks. 'I dressed for my job! Not
for you!'

'I'm your boss. The two are indivisible.'

'I wouldn't count on it!' Her voice tightened.

'Well, now,' he drawled softly, 'there's a challenge if
ever I heard one. That's the third time you've put all
your cards on the table! You'll never make a poker
player, Miss Swift!' His eyes mocked her. 'Stick to
looking beautiful and leave the intrigue to the big boys.
I'd hate to see you completely beaten.'

Rachel could only glare at him in silent hatred, not
trusting herself to speak.

He laughed under his breath. 'Come along. I'll show
you your new office.' He guided her along the corridor
and led her inside. Rachel looked around the office:
the smooth décor, cream carpet, cream walls, and gold
oak furniture.

'Welcome to your new home,' Damian murmured
sardonically.

'Very pretty,' she admitted tightly.

'You understand what all this machinery does, I take
it?' He strode to the gold oak dest, gestured to the
computer, printer, fax machine, telephone console.

'Of course!' Honestly, he really liked patronising
her.

'Good.' He turned, thrust his hands in the trouser
pockets of his black suit. 'Then we can get to work.
Get your shorthand skills sharpened and come through.
I have four letters to dictate.'

Rachel put her bag down beside her new desk and
chair, then followed him into his own office. Cream
carpet, cream walls, the fan of a green palm in a
terracotta pot, a huge oak desk with six telephones,

paintings on the walls by Picasso and Kandinski, both blazing with colour, and a panoramic view of Hong Kong through vast windows looking clean across the sunlit harbour to Kowloon.

Damian was seated in the dark leather swing chair behind the desk. 'Sit down,' he said softly, and put his strong hands behind his dark head, leaning back, watching her through hooded eyelids.

Rachel sat opposite him, crossed her long legs. His blue eyes followed the movement. He was unsmiling. Her heart beat with abrupt violence, sexual attraction crackling between them like electricity.

'The letters. . .' she said tightly.

He flicked those deadly blue eyes at her. Then in a cool voice he dictated the four letters while she tried to keep up with him. 'New paragraph. I suggest the sum of ten million Hong Kong dollars to begin with. . .' Her pen shot across the page, making symbols that she hoped she could decipher later on. 'Yours faithfully, etc. etc. New letter. To Mr Graham Warwick. . .'

When he had finished, Rachel's hand was aching. 'I'll just go and write these up.'

'Print them immediately,' he commanded. 'I want them in the midday post. Also, take these files and study them. I'll question you about them in one hour.'

Rachel went back to her desk, determined to earn her pay and prove to him that she was an efficient secretary. The word processor was easy to operate, and she had typed and printed the letters in fifteen minutes. She then turned her attention to the files, reading them carefully, answering the telephones whenever they rang, and checking with Damian to see if he was officially available or not.

'Hello?' purred a very cool, sexy female when she

answered the umpteenth call that morning. 'Who am I speaking to?'

'Rachel Swift, Mr Flint's new secretary. May I help you, Mrs. . .?'

'Miss,' Corrected the voice. 'Miss Domino Mei-Ling.'

Rachel tensed, holding her breath for a split second as her mind whirled back to that limousine, to Damian Flint beside her, his voice smoky and seductive: 'Domino. . .?'

'I'll just see if Mr Flint is free,' Rachel said jerkily, and she put her on hold, pressing the intercom. 'Mr Flint—I have Domino Mei-Ling on line one.'

'Put her through.'

Rachel put her through.

'Domino!' Damian's voice drawled. 'Thanks for last night. . .'

Rachel cut the connection as though burnt, then sat there, staring at the phone, wondering why she felt such intense and inexplicable reactions to everything this man did or said.

Ten minutes later, the intercom buzzed. 'Book a table for two at the Mandarin Grill for one o'clock today. Miss Mei-Ling will be arriving here at twelve forty-five. Let me know immediately she does.'

'Yes, sir,' she replied tightly. He would take her there. The fabled black and gold palace of the East— the Mandarin Hotel—where the élite habitually met.

Later, he called her in to discuss the files she had been studying. He went on to outline their current deals, leaning back in his chair, hands behind his dark head, but what he was really outlining to her was his power: he meant her to know that he was already too firmly entrenched, handling every top account at Swift, all over the world.

'As for the Shanghai Trust,' Damian concluded, 'we need more information before we even begin talks, let alone ——'

'Shouldn't Jamie handle that?' Rachel said suddenly, the name of the group ringing bells. 'He was at school with the MD, and he's done a lot of freelance work for them.'

The blue eyes narrowed. 'He's suspended from work.'

'But this is an important deal,' she pointed out. 'And he's the right man to go in and get the truth.'

'I'll be the judge of that, Miss Swift. You're my secretary, not my adviser.'

Temper flared in her eyes. 'I'm also the chairman's daughter!'

'Ah. . .' he said softly. 'I wondered when we'd get round to that.' He got to his feet, walked coolly around the desk to where she sat.

Rachel looked up at him, pulses leaping with awareness of his lean, powerful body.

'You like putting cards on the table,' he mocked, standing very close, his dark head bent to look directly into her eyes. 'And I think it's about time I played one. . .' He arched black brows. 'Just one of my aces. I'm running this firm. Not you. Not Jamie. Not even your father.'

'You may be running this firm while my father's in hospital and my uncle's in limbo,' she said tightly, 'but your position is purely a temporary one. I will eventually inherit the company, and when I do ——'

'You'll kick me out!' he drawled. 'But who can say what will happen between now and then? Why, you might even get married and ——'

'Most unlikely!' Her voice was choked with rage.

'You may change your mind!' he mocked.

'I will not change my mind, and even if I did——'

'You'd still kick me out. Yes, revenge will be sweet, I have no doubt. But in the meantime, Miss Swift, I am in control of this firm, and I come down very hard on insolent secretaries.'

She fell silent, her mouth a bitter, angry line.

'That's better,' he said softly, enjoying the exercise of power.

'It's almost lunchtime,' said Rachel thickly. 'Was there anything else, or may I go?'

'Just one thing.' His long hand moved to the back of her naked throat, making her gasp. 'I'm not keen on this pony-tail.' He flicked the white silk bow undone, his fingers running through it, inciting shivers of heat to flood her skin as he studied her through those hooded lids, and deliberately stroked one long finger down the nape of her neck and lowered his blue eyes to watch her nipples erect in fierce, unwanted response. 'Wear your hair loose in future,' he murmured, smiling mockingly, and lifted his gaze to hers with dark power. 'And that's an order!'

'Will that be all, Mr Flint?' Her voice shook with rage.

'For the moment, Miss Swift.' He straightened, eyes glittering.

Rachel got clumsily to her feet, and walked to the door although she wanted to run because her legs were shaking and she could feel his narrowed blue eyes burning into her back. She closed the door behind her and stood there, shaking from head to foot, breathing hoarsely.

The outer door opened suddenly. Rachel lifted her head, saw a woman enter, a ravishing Chinese woman with short black hair and sunglasses, a clinging black dress, blood-red lipstick.

'I am Domino Mei-Ling.' The dark glasses gave her an air of mystery. 'Mr Flint is expecting me.'

Somehow Rachel pulled herself together. 'Of course. I'll let him know you're here.' Turning, she knocked peremptorily on Damian's door, pushed it open and said tightly, 'Miss Mei-Ling is here.'

'Send her in.'

Rachel stepped out of the way as the engimatically beautiful Miss Mei-Ling walked into the office and closed the door behind her. Was she his mistress? Rachel didn't like the tension coiling in her stomach at the thought of that. It reminded her forcibly of the way she had felt when she walked into her flat and saw Damian Flint standing beside Jenny, and thought he was her secret lover. It felt like jealousy, but how could she know that? She'd never felt jealousy before. . .

Pulling herself together once more, Rachel's mouth tightened and she knew the best thing would be to get away for an hour by going to lunch and pushing all thoughts of Damian Flint from her mind.

Going out on to Des Voeux, she breathed in the hot, humid air. Noise was all around—the clatter of green metallic trams, cars blasting horns amid the skyscrapers and the heat, and people rushing everywhere.

'Wait!' a familiar voice shouted from the Swift offices. 'Rachel, wait. . .!'

She spun with a gasp to see Tony running towards her, and immediately she ran to him, flinging herself into his arms with relief at the sight of her oldest and most cherished friend.

'Tony!'

'Darling Rachel!'

They embraced, laughing, eyes shining.

Damian Flint strode out of the building towards his waiting limousine, and the mysteriously beautiful

Domino was at his side, his arm around her. He shot a
narrow-eyed look at Rachel and Tony as they clung
together.

'I hear you're back at Swift—are you really Flint's
secretary?'

Rachel was acutely aware of Damian, obviously able
to hear as he opened the rear door of his limousine for
Domino. 'Tony—can we have lunch or something. . .?'

They went up the hot, winding back streets behind
Des Voeux and ate at the California, a neon nightclub-
restaurant. Nighclubs were open all day in Hong Kong.
This one was particularly good, with white linen and
silver flatware, palm trees, excellent service, and huge
pink neon Cadillacs decorating the white walls.

Rachel quickly told him how the heart attack had
happened.

'Jamie was always self-destructive. Now it's spilling
over to destroy Charles, too,' Tony said. 'And you?
Are they still trying to tear you apart?'

'Yes, but it's not my primary concern,' she admitted.
'Damian Flint is what's really beginning to bug me. . .'
Something cautioned her against mentioning her fears
of marriage. That bothered her too. She had always
confided in Tony, but for some reason she could not
confide that.

'Don't worry,' he said firmly. 'You'll handle him. I
know you will. If you can just keep your cool, he can't
rattle you.'

Rachel lowered her lashes. 'That's the problem. I
can't keep my cool and he does rattle me!'

'You need to have some fun,' Tony decided. 'I
suggest an evening at 1997, dancing the night away!'

Rachel groaned. 'That sounds just what I need!'

'Great! Me too! The hell with jet lag—I'm going to

take you out tonight and stay up till my eyelids just droop shut!'

When she got back to the office, Damian called her in abruptly, his voice hard on the intercom. She tensed and went through. He was standing by the windows, his hands thrust into his black trouser pockets.

'I thought Radcliffe was in London,' he asked abruptly.

'He was there on business,' she said. 'He flew back today and heard I was working for you, so he —'

'Heard,' he cut in. 'Precisely.' He strode towards her, his eyes narrowed. 'Listen to me, Miss Swift, and listen carefully. Radcliffe is not a wise choice of companion for you at this particular point in your family crisis. Is that clear?'

'What. . .?' Her eyes flared with a fierce rush of temper. 'Are you trying to stop me seeing him? You must be out of your mind! I'm not going to just give up my —'

'See the boy if you must,' he said, mouth tight. 'But remember he knows every important member of the community. And he talks to them, I can assure you, on any subject that leaps into his addle-brained head.'

'How dare you?' she said, her voice choked with rage.

'Don't give him any gossip to spread around the colony,' he said flatly. 'There's enough as it is with Charles in hospital, Jamie charged with assault, and you back in Hong Kong working for me. I don't want careless talk to destabilise the shares. Now is *that* clear?'

She struggled to keep her temper as she choked out, 'Yes, sir!'

The blue eyes swept over her angrily. 'Get back to work. We've got a hectic schedule this afternoon.'

Rachel slammed the door as she left, rage jamming up in her mind. Keep my cool! she thought furiously. That's a laugh! Damian Flint does everything he possibly can to make me blow twenty-five fuses at once!

That night, Rachel went to the hospital to visit her father. He was much better, lying in bed listening to *Götterdämmerung* on his Discman.

'How was your first day as Damian's secretary?' he asked weakly, but his eyes gleamed with a new reason to live, and he listened eagerly as she told him half-truths about her new job.

No chance of persuading her father that Damian Flint was a rat and a snake, then, she thought as she took a taxi home. For the moment, she would have to put up with things the way they were.

The rest of the week passed in much the same way as that first day. Life in the office was tense, but the work was far more interesting than she had imagined it would be. She slipped into a nerve-racking routine with Damian Flint, and every day she went to see her father and found him getting better and better. Rachel kept in touch with Jamie. He was very glad to hear Charles was getting so much better—he didn't want his brother's death on his conscience, he said, and that gave Rachel a lot of hope for a future reconciliation. Although he was still charged with assault, the trial was not for two months, which gave her time to wait and discuss it with Charles once he was completely recovered. Her only light relief was Tony, who took her out every night. They went to all their favourite haunts—1997 and Rick's Café and the Go-Down—sometimes even the House of Doom in Wan Chai.

On Saturday morning, she was lounging on the terrace in a red sundress when the doorbell rang.

Nightingale skittered into the room, a can of polish in her hand, on her chirpy way to answer the door.

'Mr Damian!' she announced a moment later.

Rachel got up from the sun-lounger, her feet burning on the hot stone floor of the terrace, and stared at him through her dark glasses as he strode into the living-room.

He looked dangerously sexy in blue jeans and an open-necked white shirt, his tanned chest showing black hairs, his arms rippling with muscle and dark glasses hiding his powerful eyes. Her pulses raced with that angry awareness she felt whenever he was near. But today it was stronger, deeper, as though his casual clothes and presence in her home brought a new edge to their growing relationship of fierce sexual undercurrents and mutual hatred.

'To what,' she asked tightly, 'do I owe this privilege?'

'Your father's being released from hospital at lunch-time,' Damian drawled. 'I thought you might like to come with me to help him home.'

Her eyes flared. 'My father's being released and I'm the last to know! Well, that's just great! That's just —'

'Don't be childish,' he said flatly. 'I'm the one the hospital have contacted at every stage. That's why they called me, not you.'

Rachel felt hurt that her father had not had her contacted. After a lifetime of being emotionally devoured by him, she was suddenly discarded in favour of the detestable Damian Flint.

'Don't just stand there glowering at me,' Damian murmured sardonically. 'Do you want to come or not?'

Flushed and angry, she said tightly, 'Yes!'

'Good.' He turned on his heel, hands thrust in lean hip pockets, and performed a very smooth and deliberate exercise of power by giving orders to the amah without even glancing at Rachel. 'Nightingale — prepare Mr Charles's room for him.'

'Yes, sir, Mr Damian!'

'Put a television up there so he can watch the Hang Seng reports — and all his favourite British programmes. He tells me they're running *The Churchill Years* again. And arrange,' said Damian Flint, 'dinner for three tonight. Miss Rachel, Mr Charles and myself.'

Furious, Rachel stepped forward in her red sundress. 'Just a minute! Nobody told me any of this!'

Damian turned, his face hard. 'Your father's requests, Miss Swift. I take it you have no objection to dining with your father on his first night out of hospital?'

'Of course not!' she said angrily, reddening. 'I'd just like to be asked, that's all!'

He gave her a look of contempt that made her want to hit him. Then he drawled, 'Come on. We have to pick him up at midday.'

They drove to the hospital in his Mercedes. He sat beside her in the rear seats, a window open, the hot breeze lifting his black hair from his tanned face. She was so aware of his hard body, and of the undeniable sex appeal of those jeans and that white shirt, that she deliberately did not look at him, staring fixedly ahead while noting every detail of him as though it was being burned into her brain.

'Damned pills!' Charles was grumbling as Damian supported his weak body and helped him out to the car. 'I'm going to rattle for weeks!'

'Everything will be fine,' Damian drawled, 'so long as you relax.'

'With you in charge at Swift,' said Charles, 'I can finally relax.'

The car sped home, and her father talked happily all the way. As they pulled into the drive, Nightingale came rushing out to meet them.

'Welcome home, Mr Charles!' She was bouncing about in her short white cheong-sam, black hair framing her lovely, animated face. 'I put TV in your room, fresh flowers too, and big bowl of fruit — mango, papaya — '

'I don't want to go back to bed!' Charles said, clutching Damian's strong arm for support as he shuffled into the villa. 'I've only just got out of it! Put me on the terrace and mix me a Singapore Sling!'

'No alcohol,' Damian said coolly, leading him to the terrace.

'Ah, that's better.' Charles sank on to the sun-lounger. 'Home. . . I never tire of that view. Isn't it beautiful?'

The telephone shrilled into the silence.

'I'll get it,' said Damian, turning on his heel and striding into the living-room as though he owned the whole damned house, another exercise of power which made Rachel's blood boil. After a moment, he lifted his dark head and looked straight at her with hard, narrowed eyes. 'It's for you,' he said tightly, holding out the instrument. 'Radcliffe!'

Rachel moved to the phone, took it. 'Hello? Tony?'

'Hi, gorgeous!' his cheerful voice bounded into her ear. 'Still coming out on the junk tomorrow afternoon?'

'I wouldn't miss it for the world!' she replied, smiling.

'Great! I'll pick you up at one-thirty, then! Wear your sexiest swimsuit — the boys are all madly in love with you as usual!'

'Flatterer!' she laughed. 'I'll wear the sexiest swimsuit I can find! See you tomorrow. Bye. . .'

Turning, she almost bumped into Damian's powerful chest.

'Oh!' A hot flush burnt her cheeks. 'Eavesdropping, Mr Flint?'

'You've seen Radcliffe every night this week.'

'Spying, too?' she snapped, eyes flaring.

'I'd have to be deaf not to hear his sports car roaring up, music blasting, honking his bloody horn night after night.' His blue eyes glittered with anger. 'Where are you going tomorrow with him?'

'Out for the afternoon on his junk,' she enunciated through her teeth. 'Any objections?'

'So long as you don't gossip with him, no,' he said flatly, and turned on his heel to stride coolly out on to the terrace again, so tall he had to dodge the metal chimes that hung over the french windows.

When Rachel had recovered from the customary burst of rage which Damian Flint so effortlessly produced in her every time she saw him, she went out on to the terrace, putting on a brave smile for her father.

Charles looked round at her, his face suddenly flushed with annoyance. 'Rachel—are you seeing that young playboy Radcliffe again?'

'I thought you liked Tony!' she said, startled by his reaction. 'You've known him for years. . .we've even spent Christmas with his family!'

Her father shifted irritably. 'Well. . .that was when you were younger. You were just a child and I knew there was nothing serious between you.'

'But, Daddy——'

'You're nearly twenty-five,' Charles said, annoyance in his eyes. 'You should be thinking of marriage, selecting a suitable mate, getting ready to have children. Not running around with young tearaways like Radcliffe!'

Flushing, Rachel looked at Damian, expecting to see mockery, but he was looking at the bay, his tough profile expressionless.

She looked back at her father. 'I'm only going out on his junk with friends for the afternoon. It's just fun.'

'Fun!' He looked furious. 'I never had time for fun when I was your age! I was too busy building this company up and trying to found a dynasty! A fat lot of good it did me! My wife killed before her time, my son born dead and my only surviving heir a selfish girl who just wants to have fun!' He winced and clutched his chest. 'Damn it all. . .!'

Rachel went white, moving towards him, trembling. 'It's all right,' she said in a husky rush, alarmed by his sudden outburst, afraid for him, the memory of those wires and the heart machine vivid in her mind. 'I'll ring Tony and cancel. I'll stay home with you, look after you——'

'Don't be a damned fool!' Her father sighed heavily. 'Darling, I don't want to drive you away again with impossible demands.'

'Sssh!' Rachel was terrified, and patted his hand, trying to soothe him.

'I just worry about you, about the company, about the future. . .'

'There's no need to worry,' she said huskily, 'I promise you I'll make everything all right so you don't need to worry again.'

'But you must marry well!' he whispered, clutching her hand. 'You must. . .or everything will be destroyed!'

'I give you my word,' she said intensely, 'that I will find a man who can save Swift for us all, and then I'll marry him.'

CHAPTER FOUR

THEY ate dinner, the three of them, in the mahogany dining-room. Damian sat opposite her, and every glance at his tough face only underlined her rash promise to her. Nobody but Damian could possibly run the company. Jamie simply was not cut out for it. Oh, he was charming and debonair—but he was no match for Damian Flint. That thought irked her. In fact, it annoyed the hell out of her. More than anything, it revealed to her a suppressed but undeniable respect for Damian, and she hated knowing she respected him. It was far more convenient just to dislike him, to tell herself he was a rat, a snake, a ruthless villain. Not have to face up to the fact that he was a dynamic, intelligent, charming man with a gift for finance and the raw exercise of power. He was shifting in her mind suddenly, stepping out of the shadows she had so forcibly pushed him into in self-defence, and she realised her attraction to him was more than just physical. Angrily, she pushed her thoughts away at the same time as she pushed her bowl and chopsticks away. I don't respect Damian Flint, she told herself furiously, and I don't admire him either. He's a hard, ruthless man and I'll have nothing to do with him.

After dinner, Charles said, 'I'm so tired! Do excuse me. . .' and shuffled off to bed, helped up the stairs by Nightingale, leaving Rachel alone with Damian.

They studied one another across the dimly lit living-room.

'Brandy?' suggested Damian coolly.

'Thank you,' she said tightly, aware that her father had left them alone deliberately.

He strode across to the drinks cabinet. The polished wooden floor glowed richly, a Persian rug hand-woven in silk spread across the centre. Outside, the cicadas buzzed metallically, the sea was dark blue and only the steady hum of the air-conditioning broke the silence. Damian walked back to her, handed her her brandy glass.

'Here.' His long fingers brushed hers, sending her pulses racing.

Rachel's hand shook as she sipped her brandy. The fan overhead whirred softly, flickering strands of her black hair on to her sun-kissed shoulders, the red sundress strappy and sexy.

'That was quite a promise you made to your father tonight,' Damian said softly. 'Let's hope you can live up to it.'

'I'm sure I shall!' she said tightly, not meeting his eyes.

'Got your husband picked out already?'

'Not yet. But I can assure you I'll give it my full attention.'

'No doubt.' His smile was hard.

Rachel flicked her green eyes to meet his. There was a brief, tense silence. She was deeply aware of the impact of his hard sexuality as he stood so close, his white shirt revealing a tanned chest.

'Why should you be interested in my marital plans?' she asked abruptly. 'After all—you seem more than preoccupied with the sultry Domino.'

'Sultry?' A hard smile curved his mouth.

'Dark glasses, clinging dresses, an air of Oriental mystery. . .'

'Ah, yes,' he said softly, watching her.

'That kind of woman appeals to a lot of men. I can't think why.' Careful, she thought; watch it. You sound jealous.

'Can't you, indeed. . .?' he murmured, his eyes narrowing intently.

'No.' She gave a brittle laugh, shrugging. 'Obviously, it appeals to you, though, or you wouldn't be seeing her. Are you madly in love?'

His eyes glinted. 'We're just good friends.'

'Tony tells me it's a hot item.'

'He's a scandalmonger,' he said softly, moving closer, making her pulses rocket. 'I've told you that before.'

She was staring at his mouth suddenly. 'Domino was in London with you, wasn't she?' she said, jerking her gaze away forcefully.

'She was my secretary before you,' he said softly.

Rachel tensed. His secretary. Her hand shook. 'Well, what a coincidence! That she should hand her notice in so suddenly! After a business trip to London with the boss, all expenses paid, no doubt, but. . .well, well, well.'

He laughed softly. 'Well, well, well, indeed!'

'And I just found myself in the right place at the right time!' Her eyes were glittering through her lashes. 'One day minding my own business in London; the next, Damian Flint's new secretary!'

'Yes, wasn't that lucky!' he murmured sardonically.

'But who can predict the future?'

His eyes glinted. 'Oh, I could take a stab at it.'

'Could you?' she said tightly. 'How very clever you are, Mr Flint! Would you care to share your predictions?'

'Not right at this moment,' he drawled, and he was so close that their bodies were only inches apart, and as he looked down at her mouth with narrowed eyes she felt her heart begin to race madly.

'What a shame!' she said jerkily, trying hard not to show how much he was rattling her. 'Because we could share predictions, you and I. You never know—your infamous luck might one day run out!'

'Is that so?'

'Yes!' she said tightly. 'Someone not so far from here might just decide to take all those opportunities you wax so lyrical about away from you!'

'Well, who would do such a thing?'

'Not me,' she murmured mockingly.

'Not much!'

Rachel laughed, breathless for some reason. 'I'd have to hate you to even consider it!'

'Yes,' he said softly, his eyes darkening. 'And hate is a very powerful emotion, Miss Swift. Very powerful indeed. You don't feel anything of that nature for me . . .do you?'

'No, I most certainly do not!' Her eyes moved contemptuously over him, and then started to flicker, dart, race over him, staring fixedly as she realised his clothes were irrelevant; she had X-ray vision, could see through his shirt, see every muscle, sinew, black hair. . . Her pulses raced with alarm. 'I—I don't feel anything like. . .' She tried to get her mind to work, looking up at his face. 'Like. . .like hatred for you. I. . .' Suddenly, she was staring at that mouth. Suddenly, she wasn't smiling any more. And suddenly her heart was beating very fast, slamming against her ribcage like a demented hammer.

He stepped closer, unsmiling, slowly slid strong hands on her waist.

She swallowed. 'I don't. . .' she whispered, struggling to think as she blindly put her hands on his

shoulders, staring at his chest, his tanned throat, and
then his mouth. . .his mouth. . .his mouth. . .

Damian Flint slowly lowered his dark head.

His mouth met hers and her shocked little gasp
turned to a moan of hunger as she closed her eyes and
kissed him at last, *at last*, and the brandy glass fell from
her hands, shattering at their feet as her arms went
around his neck, her mouth opening hungrily beneath
his, her hands in his black hair, her body pressing
against his as they clung together with intolerable
necessity, unaware of the fragments of glass they
trampled as Damian pressed her tighter, tighter until
there was not an inch between their bodies. She heard
his harsh breathing, the rough exclamations of his own
excitement as he kissed her deeper, his hands moving
up her spine, thrusting into her thick black hair, blind
passion exploding between them after so long. It had
always been there, the need to kiss, to touch, growing
in hot, dark secrecy from the minute they met.

'Oh, God. . .!' Damian said in a voice thick with
desire, dragging air into his lungs momentarily, staring
at her with glittering eyes before his mouth claimed
hers again, deeper, more demanding, and Rachel's
fingers were stroking his throat, her mouth moving
blindly against his, and she felt his hands on her hips,
hard and shaking, pressing her against him until she
felt the evidence of his own fierce excitement hard
against her. His hands left her hair, moved swiftly
down her spine, cupping her rear suddenly and pressing
her tighter against his hard body, a harsh groan coming
from the back of his throat as one strong hand swept
suddenly to her breast, and as he touched and stroked
her there she gave a fierce moan of excitement, whispering incoherent words against his mouth in blind,
overpowering, dazed response.

'You want more coffee, Mr——?' Nightingale's light voice broke off abruptly and her footsteps halted on the parquet floor.

They broke apart, flushed and breathless. Rachel stumbled back, eyes dazed, mouth bruised, her heart banging violently.

Damian raked a strong hand through his dark hair and turned. 'Get the hell out of here!'

Nightingale scurried away with a bob.

Rachel moved with a hoarse cry, groping blindly for support, trying to reach the sofas, shaking like a leaf. How had that happened? The blood was pumping violently through her body; she was knocked for six. . .

Damian followed her in three quick strides, reached for her.

'No!' she burst out hoarsely, leaping back from his hard hand. 'Don't touch me!'

He was darkly flushed. 'You didn't seem to mind just now!'

'I didn't know what was happening!' she whispered huskily.

'Yes, you did,' he said thickly, reaching for her. 'Come back here. . .'

'No!' She was backing, slapping his hand away, shock in her eyes. 'I want to forget this happened. Just forget——'

'You didn't expect it to happen,' he said under his breath. 'Neither did I, but it did, and now you're scared because you can see how far it would have gone if Nightingale hadn't——'

'No!' The word shot from her swollen lips; she was still reeling with shock. 'It was a one-off thing! It'll never happen again!'

'Oh, yes, it bloody well will!' he said thickly, and

caught her by the wrist, dragging her against his hard body.

She fought him, wanting him, hating him, intolerably confused, her voice shaking as she denied everything. 'It was chance! It meant nothing! I'm drunk, I'm tired, I'm——'

'Attracted to me!' His strong arms were around her as she struggled. 'Well, what the hell is wrong with that? Kiss me again, for God's sake.' He bent his head suddenly, his mouth hot on her shivering neck.

'Oh, God. . .' she whispered in ecstasy, her head tilting back as he ravaged her bare throat. Her hand clutched his dark head. It felt unbearably good to hold him as he kissed her. 'Don't. . .don't. . .'

He raised his head, darkly flushed, and his eyes glittered. 'I want this just as much as you do.'

She stared into that tough face and her first thought was, *Do* you? It seemed inconceivable that a man as fantastic as Damian Flint could find her attractive, and as she realised that that was what she truly thought of him she felt her hands move caressingly on his strong throat and her eyes move down unsteadily to study his mouth.

'Yes. . .!' he said deeply, and then his mouth closed over hers, burningly sensual as his hands moved slowly up to tunnel into her thick black hair, and as her mouth opened beneath his the hunger swept them both again, their breathing quickening as the kiss took fire and his mouth was fierce, hot, demanding, his hands moving over her body as she heard his heart thudding violently at his chest, and she knew she was in danger of losing her mind with the sweet, hot rush of excitement.

The blood raced through her, she heard herself moan hoarsely, shaking, her mouth opening hungrily, and then she felt the fear whirl up inside her like a typhoon.

'I said don't!' she shouted hoarsely, and slapped him around the face with a stinging blow that sent his head jerking back, black hair falling over his tanned forehead.

Silence.

They stared at each other. Rachel was shocked, angry, confused. Damian was just as angry, and his eyes leapt with blue rage as he stared down at her.

For a second, she thought he might force her to respond, and she shrank visibly, her voice hoarse as she said, 'I don't want you!'

'Some other time, then,' Damian bit out tightly. 'I'm sure I can think of someone else who'll be more than willing to admit they want me instead of playing hard to get!' He angrily thrust her away from him, turned on his heel and walked out of the villa without another word.

Rachel sank shaking on to the white sofa and buried her hot face in her hands. How had it happened? One minute they were sworn enemies, the next they were clinging together in fierce mutual desire.

Her trembling fingers traced his kiss on her lips. She remembered her thoughts as he told her he was as shocked as her, and that he wanted it to continue. . . her heart skipped beats frantically. A man like that? So sexy, charming, mercurially intelligent. . . God, he was gorgeous — and he wanted her. She felt breathless.

Then she remembered he was just using her to get the company, to get her to marry him!

The realisation made her face burn with shame and humiliation. How could she have let him do that? Oh, God, she'd never be able to live it down. She felt such a fool A stupid, naïve little idiot. She hated him, hated him, her respect and breathless excitement keeling over under the weight of her rage and humiliation.

And now he was going to that witch Domino. He'd said as much, the callous swine, flinging his mistress at her deliberately. He knew that it would make her feel inferior and stupid and insignificant beside the sultry Domino and her no doubt dazzling sexual experience!

How she hated him!

Next day, her father was all smiles as they ate breakfast on the terrace in the morning sun.

'I hear you and Damian got on famously last night!'

Her face burnt. Bad news travelled fast. Silently, she concentrated on cutting her mango into thin strips.

'You're blushing,' he said, pleased. 'That tells me all I need to know.'

When she was alone on the terrace, she found herself staring fixedly at a cockroach as it scuttled around in the heat, then got up and hammered it to death with her shoe. Then she straigtened, dropped her shoe with a clatter, shaking. . .what was happening to her?

At midday Damian arrived for lunch. Rachel's face burned as she met his eyes then quickly looked away. The swine looked even more attractive than ever in a black open-necked polo shirt and black jeans. She remembered last night's kiss and went scarlet, her hand shaking as she tried to eat her salad. How completely he had humiliated her. She wanted to throw her lunch at his self-assured face.

'How's Domino?' she asked tightly as they all three sat drinking coffee on the terrace. 'Did you see her last night?'

His eyes narrowed.

'Domino?' Charles frowned, looking at Damian. 'What on earth is she talking about?'

'Just a little private joke,' drawled Damian Flint with a mocking smile that made Rachel hate him even more.

After lunch, she hurriedly excused herself and went upstairs, feeling demented.

Tony picked her up in his cherry-red convertible. She leapt into the front seat in a skimpy white sundress, glad to escape the house. They drove down to Causeway Bay where his junk was waiting, and were taken out to it in a sampan owned by an ancient Chinese in a lampshade hat.

It was a beautiful day, and the junk was absolutely full of all her old friends. They all sat around on deck drinking punch and asking Rachel the usual questions.

'How's old Blighty?'

'Still raining all summer long?'

They sunbathed and swam, music played on the stereo, and the junk sailed past the skyscrapers and hills of Hong Kong Island. Most of Tony's male friends flirted with Rachel, and she flirted back lightly, but knew she wasn't remotely interested in any of them. Damian Flint had shown her that with just one kiss.

At six, they all left the junk and Tony drove her home, up over the Causeway Bay flyover, the hot wind in her wet hair.

Suddenly, Rachel saw Tiger Balm Gardens and realised they were on Tai Hang Road. 'Tony — would you drop me at Jamie's apartment?' she heard her voice saying. 'It's just a few blocks further. . .'

'Sure. Why not?' Seconds later, the red convertible nipped into the private drive to the apartment block hidden by fringed jacaranda trees.

Jamie answered on her first buzz, and the door clicked open for her. She waved goodbye to Tony, then went straight up.

'This is a surprise!' Jamie greeted her with a kiss and a hug.

Rachel said huskily, 'Jamie, I'm in trouble. I need to talk to you.'

He sobered instantly, taking her arm and leading her to the wrought-iron balcony. 'Sit down. Tell me all about it.'

'My father came home yesterday,' she told him in a rush. 'I'm frightened for him. He snaps and frets and worries himself into a frenzy. I can see why he had that heart attack. I can also see another one just around the corner.' She took a shaky breath, looked up at her uncle. 'Then last night I made this promise to him. Stupid of me, really, but I was so desperate to make him lie down and relax that I——'

'What promise?' asked Jamie, suddenly very still.

Rachel looked away. 'I promised I'd find the right man to save Swift and then marry him.'

The warm breeze whispered through the chimes hanging from the balcony ceiling. Far below, beyond the fringed jacaranda, Hong Kong's white skyscrapers sparkled in a faint sunlit mist.

'Jamie,' she said, 'there's only one man capable of running Swift.'

He went white, fingered his shirt collar restlessly.

'I'm running out of time.' Rachel watched his face. 'My father can't take much more strain. I have to act fast.'

Jamie suddenly got to his feet, went to the railing, thrust his hands into the pockets of his white trousers, looked out across the city.

Rachel got up too, went to him, leant on the black wrought-iron balcony railing. 'I have to save my father's life. If marrying the right man is what will save him — how can I refuse?'

He turned to look at her then, bitterness in his blue

eyes, and said, 'I hear the name Damian Flint marching inexorably into this conversation.'

She was silent, studying his face, the bitter eyes and the lines of debauchery at his mouth. Once, he had been strong, but the years of competition and jealousy showed on his face and he was losing, losing fast.

'I thought you hated him,' Jamie said thickly. 'But you don't, do you? You're beginning to consider marrying the bastard and——'

'That's not true!' she said hotly, flushing.

'What a betrayal! From you of all people!' His mouth shook. A film of tears suddenly welled in his eyes.

His words hurt her, though she knew they were true. 'I don't want to marry Damian Flint, but it might be my only choice. I can't bear to think that you'd see it as a betrayal. You know I love you and——'

'Of course,' he said in a brittle, polite voice. 'But I really think you should leave now. I have to get changed to go out tonight. Dancing at the Go-Down, you know.'

Rachel walked out on to the main road a few minutes later feeling overwhelmed with guilt. The heat made her white dress stick to her. She wandered aimlessly along until a red and silver taxi cruised past. She hailed it, gave the Chinese driver her address in a monotone, and sank back in the air-conditioned interior, staring at the white skyscrapers below.

The tug of war was still going on, just as fiercely as it ever had, only now Charles was tugging her towards Damian Flint while Jamie hurled accusations of betrayal.

A sigh broke from her throat as the taxi turned into the courtyard of the villa and the fountain played coolly in the sweltering heat. She got out, paid the driver, and tried to think about her increasingly uncertain future without feeling afraid.

As she entered the villa, her heart thudded with abrupt violence when she saw that Damian Flint was still there, in the living-room, playing chess with Charles.

'Hello, darling,' Charles called cheerfully. 'Come and watch Damian thrash me at chess. He always does, you know!'

Damian lifted hooded blue eyes to look at her, and as their eyes met she felt her body tremble, heat rushing through her. He just looked so intolerably sexy, lounging on the white sofa, his body lean and powerful, the open-necked black polo shirt drawing the eye to that muscle-packed chest, his black jeans enhancing his long legs.

All right, she thought angrily, so I find him attractive. So what? That doesn't mean I feel anything else for him. It's just a powerful attraction and I can fight it. I certainly don't have to let him take advantage of it or let him bludgeon me into a marriage that would be power-based and intolerable.

Then Damian's blue eyes flicked over her body in a hot way that sent her heart racing and her legs trembling. I can't fight it, she realised with horror. There's nothing I can do. . .

'Well, sit down, then,' said her father.

'I. . .' Her voice was husky. 'I have to take a shower before dinner!'

'OK, darling.' Her father studied the chessboard. 'But don't take too long. Dinner's in an hour, and Nightingale's gone to a lot of trouble. She's doing Damian's favourite—Peking duck.'

Rachel tensed. 'Damian's favourite?'

'Yes, he's staying for dinner again.'

'Checkmate!' Damian said softly as he moved the black knight to trap the white king.

Dinner was an affair so riddled with undercurrents and tension that Rachel was barely able to eat the delicious tissue-thin pancakes, sliced spring onions and shredded duck Nightingale had so lovingly prepared. They drank hot sake from tiny porcelain cups, and Rachel felt light-headed from the potent Japanese alcohol.

'Well. . .' Charles yawned exaggeratedly after the meal '. . .early to bed, early to rise, and all that sort of thing!' He got to his feet, waving a hand at Damian. 'No, it's all right. I can go up myself. Have a lovely evening together, you two!'

Rachel crimsoned, watching him disappear up the stairs as she and Damian walked in tense silence to the living-room.

'Brandy?' Damian asked coolly, closing the living-room door.

'No, thank you!' she snapped, recognising the opening moments of last night. She was on edge as it was, heart jumping, deeply aware of that hard body, the black polo shirt that had constantly drawn her eyes during dinner, her X-ray eyes seeing every muscle, sinew, hair on his chest. Control yourself! she thought fiercely. Don't look at him. And don't think about how charming and witty he is, either. Or how strong, dynamic, intelligent, well dressed, cool, clever. . . you'll go mad if you keep listing his qualities; you'll never be able to resist him.

'No need to snap at me,' Damian's deep voice said. 'I offered you brandy because I thought it might steady your nerves.'

Hot colour flooded her face. 'My nerves don't need steadying!'

'Really? You gave quite the opposite impression over dinner.' He moved coolly to the drinks cabinet, picked up the crystal decanter.

'Is it any surprise?' she asked in a low, angry voice. 'After what happened last night? Of course I'm a little on edge. That's only natural. I don't want a repetition of——' She broke off, face burning.

He threw her a glittering look over one broad shoulder. 'It was only a kiss!'

She dragged her gaze from his. 'Yes. Only a kiss!' Her voice was thickening, and so was her breathing.

'And you've had so many kisses before!' Damian drawled, an edge to his voice. 'Every time I see you, with young Radcliffe you're in each other's arms!' He was pouring himself a brandy. 'Not to mention all the other young men you hang around with. It's quite a crowd, isn't it? What do they call themselves? Some absurd name. . .'

'The groovesome dudes,' she said thickly, staring at him through her lashes, then drew an unsteady breath and turned her back on him.

'The groovesome dudes!' he said tightly. 'How could I forget?'

Rachel kept her back to him. 'We're just friends!'

'Sure you are!' he drawled, and she heard him put his glass down with a definite clink. 'So — why the big fuss over one kiss from me?'

'I'm not making a fuss!' She sensed him walking up behind her and her pulses clamoured hotly. She spun round, eyes wide, ready to fight him off if he tried to kiss her again. 'Don't stand so close to me!' she snapped unreasonably.

'Why not?' he asked tightly, staring down at her.

'Because I know what you're trying to do, and it won't work!'

'What am I trying to do?'

'Don't play games with me,' she said in a hot rush. 'My father's made it clear enough that he wants us to — to — '

'Get on well together?' he suggested with a cynical laugh.

Her eyes flashed angrily. 'If you like.'

'I do like,' he drawled mockingly, and slid his strong hands over her waist, then pulled her hard against his powerful body. 'I like very much indeed!'

'Get your hands off me,' she said under her breath, but her heart was pumping blood round her body and her hands were already curling on his broad shoulders.

'I don't think I want to,' Damian said softly, eyes darkening. 'So what are you going to do about it?'

She swallowed. 'Slap your face again.'

'Go ahead. I can take it.'

Rachel lifted a hand, heart pounding, and tried to slap him.

He caught her wrist, his smile mocking as he held her easily. 'Too bad! I was faster. Next move is mine, I believe!' And his dark head bent, his mouth closing over hers with burning sensual expertise.

She gave a hoarse moan of resistance and desire, pushing at his broad shoulders as his strong hands pressed her hips closer to his body, and as she felt that mouth claiming hers with deeper passion, and felt the evidence of his hard excitement, she felt her body clamouring for more, her eyes closing and her mouth moving under his hungrily, little gasps of shocked desire coming from the back of her throat. God, he was so gorgeous. . .her hands were moving on to his strong thoat, thrusting into his black hair, she was losing her head again as the kiss deepened and she heard him give a low growl of harsh excitement, his

mouth increasing the pressure until Rachel was obliterated by him, dazed, clutching him with shaking hands,
gasping hoarsely against his mouth, feeling his strong
hands move swiftly up to her breasts to stroke her
nipples and force a long hoarse cry of exquisite desire
from her. His mouth dragged swiftly from hers, fell to
her throat, ravaging her hot, shivering neck, his hand
tugging down the bodice of her dress ready to expose
her to his expert hands and mouth.

Suddenly, she was fighting her way out of the hot
embrace, pushing at his hard shoulders, her swollen
lips muttering, 'No! I won't let you do this!'

'Don't fight me,' he said huskily, face flushed and
eyes glittering like blue needles as he held on to her
easily, his mouth burying in her hair, his heart thudding
hard at his strong chest.

She wanted to give in, weaken, her eyes closing and
her fingers curling on his hard shoulders. Then she
remembered what he really wanted from her and her
rage burst forth like fire.

'You're only after the company! This is ambition and
I'll have none of it!' Her voice shook as she slapped
and struggled her way free, then turned on her heel
and ran to the stairs, almost slipping in her high heels.

He caught her wrist, bit out raggedly, 'This has
nothing to do with the company! It's between you and
me!'

Nothing he could have said could have terrified her
more; it meant he wanted to take her to bed as well as
take her self-respect and her father's company.

'I don't care what it is!' she spat hoarsely. 'I won't
let it happen—now get your hands off me before I
scream loud enough to wake the guards at the Chinese
border!' Her eyes warred with his. 'I mean it, Damian.

I'll scream my head off if you don't let go and I won't stop screaming!'

His mouth tightened but he released her wrist, eyes glittering, and she ran up the stairs, into her bedroom, slammed the door, locked it, then knew with a terrible deep certainty that she had run from her own desire.

Facing him at the office next day was like facing a firing squad. She got out of the taxi on Des Voeux and handed the driver a crumpled fistful of Hong Kong dollars. In her state of extreme nervous tension she had clutched those dollars so tightly that they'd almost disintegrated.

When she arrived in the outer office, she sat at her desk, trembling, hoping Damian would not appear all day, but of course she was lying to herself again, appalled by her own desire.

His door opened suddenly.

Rachel's eyes shot to him, her heart thudding violently.

He was wearing one of his Savile Row suits, the cut of that grey cloth superb, fitting his muscular body to perfection. She was reminded forcibly of the air of absolute power that he projected so effortlessly in his professional life.

'Come in here, Miss Swift,' he said, unsmiling. 'Immediately.'

Rachel got to her feet, pen and notepad in hand, forcing herself to keep her disintegrating professional cool as she followed him into his luxurious modern office overlooking the city.

'I'm afraid a crisis has whirled up in our Auckland office.' He stood by the window, hands thrust in trouser pockets, hard profile averted to study the tall gold skyscraper on the harbour front.

'What sort of crisis?' she asked tautly.

'A New Zealand millionaire by the name of Forster.'
Still he did not look at her, a muscle jerking in his
cheek. 'He's heard of your father's heart attack, and
wants reassurance — personal reassurance — that I will
be the next chairman of the international network,
which of course includes all dealings in Auckland.'

Rachel moistened her lips. 'You'll have to fly out
there, then?'

'Yes. But a personal reassurance from me will not
be acceptable unless it's backed up by a member of the
Swift family.'

Her pulses began to pick up faster, faster. . .

'Your father couldn't possibly make the journey.
Jamie would flatly refuse. That leaves only one other
person.' He turned his dark head in time to see the
colour drain from her face as her green eyes filled with
fear and excitement. 'You'll have to come with me to
Auckland for three days, Rachel.'

She struggled not to run screaming from the office,
seeing the trip ahead, knowing what would happen,
that desire, that overpowering excitement flaring up
between them in a hotel bedroom somewhere on the
other side of the world, dragging her deeper into a
relationship that was already tearing her to pieces.

Yet she could not refuse to go. The rumours about
Swift were already reaching a crescendo on every
stockmarket in the world. Until Charles Swift's successor was offically named, the shares would remain
hovering in uncertainty, ready to plummet.

'Will you agree to accompany me?' Damian asked
abruptly.

Her voice shook. 'Where will we be staying?'

'The Auckland Regent,' he said, mouth hard. 'In
separate bedrooms, of course.'

'Of course!' she said tightly, and felt the heat flood

her cheeks betrayingly. Looking down at her red shoes, she said, 'You're right. This is an emergency. I know Forster. . .he'll talk to the Press if we don't reassure him.' She drew an unsteady breath, lifted her dark head, looked him in the eye. 'Yes, Damian. I will go to Auckland with you and represent my family at this meeting.'

Damian watched her in silence, a hard smile on his ruthless mouth. She was openly acknowledging him as Charles Swift's successor and his eyes glittered with the knowledge.

Rachel turned her back, walked to the door without another word, and when she had closed it behind her she leant on it, drawing shaking breaths. I had no choice, she told herself. I had to be brave, had to think of the company, of my father — not myself.

But when she got to Auckland, when she found herself alone with Damian for three days and three nights. . .what would she think of then?

I'll think of him, she realised, appalled. I already think of nothing but him, but this will be different; this will surpass everything else.

He'll be there, night and day. I'll see him at rest, at work, at play. Tired, irritated, angry. Relaxed, laughing, carefree. In formal clothes and in jeans. And the conversations we'll have might just tip the balance from strong sexual attraction and growing respect into something new and deeper. . .

Fear engulfed her. Resist him, she told herself. Resist him and keep remembering that he only wants you to further his ambitions. . .

CHAPTER FIVE

AUCKLAND was bathed in sunset, a city of white bridges, modern buildings, yachts, trees and dappled water. Their hotel was in a wide tree-lined street in the centre of town, surrounded by pretty cafés, restaurants and boutiques. Damian's room was directly next to hers, and Rachel looked ahead to the next three nights with fear and excitement. The journey with him had been tense, the atmosphere between them like standing on the edge of a volcano, waiting to be flung into the fire when it exploded.

They had dinner at the hotel restaurant on their first night. As they ate, he said, 'I spoke to your father before we left. He's dropping the charges against Jamie. He's back at work now in the Hong Kong offices.'

Rachel looked at him in sudden shock. Had he really done that? She could hardly believe him capable of such kindness. In fact—she didn't dare. If she ever believed that of him, she would weaken, give in to the powerful attraction, and then she would have to admit there were emotions behind that attraction, emotions that would lead her into heartbreak. She shut them off instinctively, like slamming a door, with ruthless determination never to feel anything but hatred for Damian Flint.

'You never do anything without a motive,' she said tightly. 'Good or otherwise. I wonder why you did that to help Jamie?'

The blue eyes glittered. 'Your opinion of me is just about rock bottom, isn't it?'

After the meal, they went back upstairs. Riding up in the lift, she was prickling with heat from head to foot, intensely aware of his lean, powerful body beside her.

'If we're lucky,' Damian drawled, leaning against the lift wall and watching her from below hooded lids, 'we might sort out Forster in one day. Then we could spend some time together.'

'I'll hope and pray that we don't!' she said, her voice unsteady.

'Oh, surely not,' he mocked, and the softly spoken words, combined with the look in his eyes, made her heart leapt with sudden violence.

The lift doors slid open.

'Goodnight,' she said, almost running out of the lift to her room and shaking with relief when she closed and locked the door behind her.

Next morning, a chauffeur-driven limousine picked them up after breakfast. Did Damian ever go anywhere without one? she wondered. He had a taste for power, and a gift for exercising it. Powerful men are a breed apart, she thought suddenly, and remembered Fitzgerald's quote about the rich being different. Looking at Damian Flint, she knew he was not different because he *had* power: he was different because he wanted it, fought for it, and knew how to use it. That respect and admiration was creeping back into her mind and heart. Her face drained of colour. She slammed the door ruthlessly on respect and embraced hatred again.

The Swift offices were of grey marble and gleamed under cool sunlight. They walked through the palatial foyer, then took the chairman's lift up to the top floor.

As they entered the boardroom, executives swarmed around Damian.

'Mr Flint—I have some proposals for you to study.'

'Mr Flint—can I get you some coffee?'

'Mr Flint——'

Rachel was forgotten and ignored. Suddenly, Damian turned his dark head to look at her with narrowed eyes. He saw the knowledge in her face that he was already chairman—all he needed was the official confirmation. A hard smile touched his mouth, a smile that made her heart skip beats.

He strode to her, took her wrist in a hard hand. 'This is Miss Swift. She will sit beside me during the meeting. Get her a chair and some coffee.'

Everyone clamoured to say hello to her. Men fell over themselves to get a chair. Rachel's eyes locked with Damian's in a moment of recognition of the extent of his power. Her legs felt weak. She was fighting him so hard, resisting him with everything she had. But there were moments when he got through her barriers, and, although they were rare, this was one of them. And look at her. . .turning soft with admiration for a man who cared for nothing but his ambition.

After the board meeting, they drove fifty miles south of Auckland to meet Forster for lunch. Kurt Forster was an impressive man, tall and tanned and wiry with fierce green eyes and shaggy blond hair. Lunch was served in a palatial room with gold mirrored walls, crystal chandeliers, and huge french windows overlooking acres of sunlit, sheep-dotted farmland.

The two men discussed the future of Swift.

'Do you think Charles will abdicate?'

Damian studied him expressionlessly. 'It would seem the obvious move.'

'He's mentioned it to you, Damian?'

'Several times.' He inclined his dark head.

'Glad to hear it. God knows, it would be a disaster if Jamie took over. He's a nice guy, but he'd ruin Swift within five years.'

'I don't think there's any chance of Jamie becoming chairman,' Damian drawled coolly, and flicked his piercing blue gaze to Rachel. 'Do you?'

Her eyes met his. This was her moment, and she knew she had no choice but to take it. 'No. . . Jamie will never be chairman.'

'Who will, Rachel?' Kurt watched her with narrowed eyes.

She didn't even hesitate. 'Damian Flint,' she clipped out, and Damian met her eyes with a hard smile. Her hand shook as she put her wine glass down. She wanted to throw the glass at him and shout, Get away from me! Stop affecting me like this, attacking me on all fronts with your damned charm and intelligence and unbelievable sex appeal! But of course she couldn't; she had to sit there and be polite, supporting him as the next chairman, knowing that was exactly what he was, knowing no one could handle the job better, and knowing too that he was one day going to get around to handling *her*. . .superbly. She steeled herself against him, ready for that devastating move when it eventually came.

They left Kurt Forster's at seven o'clock that night.

'That went better than I expected,' said Damian as the limousine swept back to Auckland. 'We don't need to see him again until Thursday. That gives us the day off tomorrow.' He gave her a mocking smile. 'I'll hire a car. We can drive off alone and see the sights.'

Her pulses leapt with a ferocity that alarmed her. Alone!

'Meanwhile,' Damian said coolly, 'I suggest we cele-

brate our victory with a serious night on the town. I'll
meet you in the downstairs bar at nine. Wear one of
your. . .many sexy dresses.'

She flushed, pulses leaping. 'A night on the town?
And I thought you were only interested in money and
ambition!'

'Oh, I can assure you I play just as hard as I work!'

Later, in her bedroom, she dressed in a tight red
velvet dress with a plunging sweetheart neckline. It was
just above knee-length and fitted her slender curves
perfectly.

They met downstairs at nine.

Damian was standing by the bar, broad-shouldered
and superb in a black evening suit, tight black waistcoat, a red carnation in his lapel. He looked so
gorgeous that she tripped as she reached him in her
high red heels, and landed against his hard chest with
a gasp of shocked pleasure.

'I always catch a lady when she falls,' he said softly,
his strong hands steadying her. 'Especially in a dress as
sexy as that!'

Rachel wrenched herself out of his embrace, aware
of the barman watching them with an indulgent smile,
as though they were lovers, not enemies. To Damian
she said tightly, 'Shall we go?'

He had booked a table at the best restaurant in
Auckland. The limousine took them there and they ate
oysters, the local delicacy, followed by grilled lobster
with salad at a table overlooking the marina.

'There's a superb nightclub on the other side of the
marina,' Damian told her as they drank coffee after
their meal. 'We'll go there after we've had our
liqueurs.'

Rachel looked at him through her lashes. 'Damian

Flint, chairman of the board, in a nightclub?' she mocked softly.

'I like the pulse of nightclubs,' he drawled. 'They're sexy, gutsy, dynamic. Besides—dancing is good for you. *Mens sana in* —'

'A healthy mind in a healthy body?'

'And I take care of my body!'

Rachel's gaze drifted helplessly to the hard muscles of his chest.

Damian watched her. 'There's a gym installed at my villa. I lift weights every morning before I go into the office.'

'You must be very fit,' she said in an odd tone, staring at his chest.

'Yes,' he said softly, 'I work up quite a sweat.'

She pictured him working up a sweat.

There was a little silence.

'Shall we go?' Damian's deep voice drawled, and Rachel suddenly realised she was clutching her glass so tightly that the stem might have cracked.

Flushed, she got to her feet. 'Yes, why not?'

They walked in the cool, tranquil night air together. The boats in the marina bobbed, well lit, white light dappling the dark waters. The street was lined with cafés and restaurants.

'So,' drawled Damian as they strolled along, 'tell me how you keep your sensational figure, Rachel.'

'Ballet.' Her red high heels were clicking on the pavement. 'I wanted to be a ballerina when I was a child. What little girl doesn't?' She was talking too much to cover her awareness of him. 'But it was too much hard work and sacrifice, so I gave it up when I was sixteen. I still do *barre* exercises for an hour a day, though.'

'No wonder you're so graceful,' he observed coolly,

and she shot him a quick look through her lashes as he
strolled beside her, tall and very desirable, his black
hair lifting slightly in the breeze. He thought she was
graceful. . .she felt idiotically breathless, flattered,
confused — and even more alarmed than ever. He just
wants the company, not you! she told herself fiercely.
It's ambition talking, that's all — ambition.

The nightclub was dark and exclusive and filled with
beautiful people. Huge space-age lights came down
from the ceiling to flash in time to the thudding pulse
of the music. Damian led her to a long dark blue velvet
sofa and ordered a bottle of Laurent-Perrier champagne, which was brought to their table in a silver ice-
bucket.

The cork popped discreetly. Damian poured champagne into their two glasses, raised his and drawled,
'To our victory!'

'Our victory?' Rachel challenged tightly, her eyes on
his ambitious face. 'Don't you mean yours?'

His eyes narrowed. 'I think you'll benefit from any
victory of Swift. It is, after all, your family firm.'

'True.' She watched him with angry green eyes. 'But
just think how much more enjoyable your victory
would be if you were a member of the family, and it
were your family firm!'

There was a momentary silence.

'Just think,' she said, smiling, 'how it would feel if
you were head. . .of the family.'

The beat pulsed on through the nightclub, lights
flashing, illuminating Damian's sardonic smile.

'Or have you,' Rachel said under her breath, 'already
considered the prospect?'

His eyes glittered. 'No. . . I'm too busy considering
other — more exciting — prospects!' he reached out
then, and his hand curved over her wrist. 'Let's dance.'

Rachel's pulses thundered as she allowed him to lead her to the dance-floor beneath the flashing lights.

As they turned to face each other, the music ended.

Roxy Music blasted out. Damian caught her wrist, flicked her hard against him. The brief contact made her gasp. He moved, spun her away from him, caught her with an arm clamped around her waist, and slid her effortlessly up and down his hard thigh as the beat thudded rythmically and Bryan Ferry sang on, urging them to stick together. The saxophone took off again, Damian flicked her away from him, spun her back, and she was breathless with excitement, her body his to command — and how he commanded it! — as Jerry Hall began to shout like a Spanish gypsy, while a harmonica came rolling in to harden the beat.

She was flicked back against him, clamped closer with one powerful arm, and as he looked down at her, hard and intent, he made brief, rhythmic movements, flexing chest and thigh muscles to make her slide down his body, her heart hammering. . .he was practically making love to her on the dance-floor. As the music came to a thundering climax, Damian bent her back over one arm, his tough face very close to hers.

They stayed like that for a few seconds, both breathing hard, their mouths almost touching. Another song started. It was slow, romantic, sexy. Slowly, Damian straightened, lifting her back to her feet.

She could barely stand. His arms slid around her waist. Shaking, she clung to him, her hands winding around his strong neck, and they moved together, their bodies caught in the fierce tension of their rapidly accelerating desire for each other. As his thighs moved against hers, she buried her hot face in his neck, barely able to breathe. I mustn't want him this much. . . I mustn't.

Later, they walked back to the waiting limousine,
and drove back. They studied each other in the dark
car, their faces taut, their eyes glittering over each
other.

At the hotel, Damian guided her into the lift,
towered over her and said thickly, 'May I suggest a
nightcap in my room?'

'No, you may not!' Her voice shook.

He was very close, watching her intensely. Suddenly,
his gaze dropped to probe the scented hollow between
her breasts. She gave a husky exhalation of breath, and
a second later he had bent his head to press his hot
mouth against the swell of her breasts.

Rachel whispered something incoherent. Her shaking hand moved up to clutch his dark head. That hot
mouth moved over her hot, shivering skin, inciting
fierce moans of desire as she stroked his dark hair.

He lifted his head, darkly flushed, and his mouth was
on hers, opening her lips hungrily while she gasped,
pressing against him, her hands in his hair, on his
strong neck, his shoulders, blind to everything but her
own overpowering excitement.

The lift doors opened. They went on kissing, falling
against the lift wall, Damian's hard thigh thrust
between hers as he lifted her, her heart thudding
violently at his chest, moving his hard body against her
soft, arching female body while she moaned hoarsely.

The lift doors slid shut, then open again.

Damian raised his head, breathing hard. 'Come to
my room!'

'No,' she said hoarsely, and wriggled against his hard
thigh, trying to get away, her body lifted and half
splayed by his.

'Oh, God, don't move like that,' he bit out roughly,

his hands tightening on her hips as he lowered his head, mouth hungrily seeking hers.

Rachel slapped his face in blind panic, and as his head jerked back she wrenched herself from him, stumbling out of the lift, flushed and dazed, fumbling with the key at her door.

'Stop running from it, you little coward!' Damian was behind her, catching her shoulders in hard hands, spinning her to face him. 'Don't you know you'll only make it worse?'

'No!' she choked out, struggling to get away from him. 'Get away from me, you ruthless, avaricious ——'

'It's happening to both of us!' he bit out.

'It's the company! You just want the company!'

'Are you crazy?' he said thickly, darkly flushed. 'With your arms around my neck I can't think of anything but ——' He broke off as a door opened along the corridor, his head turning automatically to look away, and in that moment she escaped, going into her room and slamming the door behind her.

'You little ——!' Damian rattled the handle, banged on the door, his voice angry. 'Open this damned door and let me in!'

Rachel backed from it, shaking. 'No, Damian! You can stand there all night if you want, but I won't open my door to you!'

'Open it or I'll break it down!' he bit out, slamming a hand on it violently.

'Go ahead!' she said hoarsely, backing further. 'Let's see what the management have to say! Let's see what the newspapers have to say!'

'I'm not frightened of the management — or the bloody newspapers!'

'All right!' she threatened, feeling cornered. 'Let's

see what my father has to say when I tell him you
broke down a hotel door and tried to rape me!'

There was an angry silence. Then Damian said
bitingly, 'When it finally happens between us, Rachel,
it won't be a rape, it'll be a landslide and you know it!'
He thumped the door angrily, then she heard his brisk
footsteps as he strode to his own room next door and
slammed the door behind him with a crash.

Rachel staggered to the bed and slumped on it. She
had no idea how to cope. How could she keep resisting
him when she turned to fire under his powerful gaze,
let alone his touch? The way he'd looked down at her
breasts so suddenly in that lift. . .oh, God, it made her
tremble with heat and excitement just to remember it.
Her experience of men was limited to indifferent kisses
from kind, sweet men who made no impact on her.
Damian Flint hardly fitted into that category.

'Seduce you? It's the smart move, Rachel. You're
the key to his future.'

Jamie's prophetic words floated back to her and she
flung herself on to the bed, staring at nothing, her body
rigid with the tension of a woman in the grip of violent,
unsated desire.

He's tearing me apart, she thought, appalled. It's
not just a physical attraction. If it were, I wouldn't feel
like this, as though I'm running, running, running,
trying to slam a door that he keeps kicking open with a
look, a word, a turn of his dark head.

She fell asleep to be claimed by hot, tortured dreams.
A dark man at a forest crossroads wearing her father's
coat and Jamie's dark glasses. She ran from him,
nightmare panic making her breathing and heartbeat
echo down the long tree-lined path until she saw the
moon shining through a stained-glass window of the
garden of Eden. A voice whispered her name. She

spun, sweating with panic, to see Damian in the forest clearing. As he stepped forward to kiss her, the stained-glass window shattered and they began to make fierce, hot love on the dusty grass of the forest.

Rachel screamed and woke up, drenched with sweat, shaking, staring into space. It was morning. The horror receded as she came back to reality, breathing hard, glad of her cream duvet and calm hotel surroundings. Just a dream. . .only a dream. . .

Suddenly, she heard a door wrenched open, foot-steps running, and then Damian banging loudly at her door, rattling the handle. 'Rachel! What happened? Are you all right?'

Trembling, she called, 'Yes, I'm fine, and I'm not letting you in!'

'I heard you screaming!' he bit out harshly. 'What the hell's going on in there? Is someone with you? Is —'

'I had a nightmare!' she said quickly, and got out of bed, padding barefoot to the door. 'That's all. . .just a bad dream.'

There was a tense silence.

'What about?' he demanded thickly. 'What did you dream?'

She swallowed convulsively, her hand tracing the door as though it were him. 'It doesn't matter. . .'

'It does to me!' he said under his breath, then, after a pause, rattled the handle again, his voice softening. 'Let me in. . .'

Temptation beckoned, her eyes closed, she leaned weakly against the door, heart pounding. Suddenly, she remembered the stained-glass window shattering Eden and leapt away as though burnt. 'No, Damian! Now just go away and leave me alone!'

'Hell!' He slammed a hand on the door, then said

bitingly, 'I'll see you at breakfast in twenty minutes!'
His footsteps strode away, his door slammed.

Rachel winced at the slam of his door. How much
longer could she go on saying no when her body was
alive with a hunger for him so deep that every pulse of
her blood screamed yes?

Dressed in a white sweater and faded jeans, Rachel
went down to breakfast, her hair a mass of fresh curls
after her shower. Damian was already there, drinking
black coffee, his face hard and unsmiling.

'Did you hire a car?' Rachel asked to break the
silence as she sat opposite him, her eyes wary.

'Yes,' he said flatly. 'Order your breakfast. I'd like
to go.'

Her eyes flashed at him, but she did as he asked. He
was obviously in a very bad mood. Presumably he
thought she ought to have let him into her room to
make love to her! Well, isn't that too bad? she thought
angrily, and remained as hostile and unfriendly as he
was.

The hire car was a white saloon. After breakfast,
Damian picked the keys up at the desk, and they
walked out into the cool sunlit morning to find the
streets busy and bright.

'Where are we going?' Rachel asked as they pulled
away into the traffic.

'Shopping,' he said flatly, mouth hard. 'Then
sightseeing.'

Very friendly, she thought, and glared stonily out of
the window. They shopped in Queen Street, the main
thoroughfare of Auckland. She bought a carved
wooden statue of a Maori warrior for her father, a
nude statuette carved from Paua shells for Jamie, and
a little Maori cruet set for Tony, amused by the fierce
faces carved on the short, fat pots.

'Tourist!' Damian said irritably, eyeing the Maori salt cellar.

Deliberately, she said, 'It's for Tony.'

His eyes narrowed, then he admired the nude statuette. 'Lovely,' he murmured, tracing the curves with one finger. 'Reminds me of Domino.'

Jealousy stung her like a wasp. 'Ah, yes!' she said tightly, aware of a sudden drumming rage in her blood, 'I'd forgotten about her! What did she have to say when you told her you were taking another woman on this little "business" trip?'

'You are my secretary,' he drawled, eyes glittering, 'and the Swift heiress. That hardly qualifies you for the title "other woman"!'

'Is that what you told Domino?'

'As a matter of fact,' he said lazily, 'I didn't tell her anything.'

'Lying by omission!' she said nastily. 'Just as ruthless in your personal as in your professional life, then?'

'Hardly ruthless!' he drawled, laughing.

They rounded the corner to where the car was parked. Rachel's stomach was clenched with sick jealousy and fear. If she had needed further proof that he was without scruples or morals in his personal life, he had just given it to her.

They got back in the car and drove away in the glittering traffic. For a long time there was silence.

'What did you tell Radcliffe about this trip?' Damian asked suddenly.

'I didn't tell him anything.'

'Lying by omission?'

'Oh, really!' she said with an angry smile. 'Don't try to use the same argument on me! Tony and I aren't in love!'

'Well, I'm not in love with Domino!' he said coolly.

'Somehow——' her eyes flared with jealousy '—that just makes your behaviour worse!'

'Why?'

There was a silence. They drove up towards the countryside, trees and fields appearing on the horizon. Rachel felt that sick jealousy coiling like acid in her stomach.

'Because she's your mistress,' she said, and her voice was thick with anger. 'Why do you think?'

His eyes narrowed. 'Is Radcliffe your lover?' he asked tightly.

She sucked in her breath. 'What. . .?'

'A simple yes or no will suffice.' His mouth was curved in a hard, mocking smile. 'If we're talking love-lives, yours is just as open to scrutiny as mine. So come on! Let's while away the hours swapping stories. Or, rather, sexual achievement records.'

She went scarlet, speechless with rage as she glared at him in the sunlit interior of the car, eyes burning over his hard profile and sexy black leather jacket.

'Forgive me,' he sneered. 'Was I a little too blunt? I thought that was what you had in mind.'

'You know perfectly well it wasn't!'

'It's certainly been in my mind for some time,' he drawled tightly. 'I'd very much like to know the extent of your experience. The way you kiss me is both——'

'Shut up!' she said thickly, shaking.

'Uninhibited yet strangely naïve.'

'I said shut up!'

'Are you as experienced as I think you are? If so,' his voice thickened, 'let's go back to the hotel and go straight to bed!'

Rachel's eyes shot to his in a moment of intensity that made her skin burn with heat. His face was flushed. His knuckles were white as he gripped the steering-wheel.

'You don't want me!' The words flew out of her mouth with fury. 'You just want Swift and everything that comes with it!'

'Ah, yes,' he drawled tightly. 'Swift Investments. The great monolith of my ambition. How could I forget?'

Rachel stared fixedly out of the window at the rising green hill and tiny cluster of houses to her left.

Suddenly, Damian said deeply, 'What was your nightmare about this morning?'

'Mind your own business!' she said through her teeth, and the car swept on, the atmosphere between them growing even more unbearable the longer she held him off.

The question was — how much longer *could* she hold him off?

CHAPTER SIX

THEY went to the lion safari park on the outskirts of Auckland, driving through a series of metal gates, along dirt tracks and rough green land. As they reached the centre of the lion enclosure, a large cage on wheels was ahead of them, and a young woman with a pitchfork was shovelling carcasses of raw meat out through the bars while adult male lions, lionesses and their cubs crowded round.

A vast carcass landed in the dust beside their car. A lion padded towards them with shaggy gold mane and blood-stained jaws, came straight up to the car window.

'Just sit still,' Damian murmured beside her.

'It won't try to break the glass, will it?' Her heart was thudding violently as the lion looked into the window of the passenger seat.

'Not unless he thinks you're after his lunch,' he drawled wryly.

Rachel stared into the lion's face, awed. Fierce yellow-green eyes stared back at her. There was an expression of terrible natural justice, and she was rendered breathless by a profound understanding of just why lions were seen as kings. The difference, she realised as she stared into those terrible eyes, was that a lion was like a bee and a tiger like a wasp. This animal would only kill to survive.

Suddenly, it growled at her, bent its great shaggy head, picked up the carcass in bloody jaws and padded away to settle on the grass, paws holding the meat down while it tore the flesh with its teeth.

'What a beautiful animal!' Rachel stared after it.

'The best,' Damian agreed coolly. 'I had a cub when I was a boy. I used to play with it until it licked my hand and took the skin off. Their tongues are —'

'You had a cub?' She turned to stare at him. 'A lion cub?'

'Sure. I was born in Africa. Lived there until I was sixteen.'

Rachel just stared at him, green eyes wide. 'Are you serious?'

'Why should I lie?' he drawled, leaning back, jean-clad thighs spread, chest outlined in the white open-necked shirt, black leather jacket gleaming under the sun.

She was helplessly fascinated and asked slowly, despite herself, 'What was it like to live in Africa?'

'The plains are ravishing,' he said flatly. 'Green landscape, gold lions, and incredible skies. What was your nightmare about last night?'

Rachel's mouth tightened. 'Stop asking me about that!'

'It made you scream. It must have been pretty memorable.'

'It wasn't. I've forgotten it.'

He gave a harsh laugh and started the car. 'Come on. Let's go. Watching the lions feed has made me rather peckish.'

They drove back into town, parked in a sunny tree-lined street with white wooden New Orleans-style buildings, art shops and trellised balcony cafés and restaurants. Damian took her to one of the balcony restaurants, and they shared a dozen fresh oysters on the shell in the cool sunlight.

'What did you do before you joined Swift?' Rachel asked suddenly as they drank black coffee, because the

question had been burning on her mind for some time,
and she told herself it was important strategically to
find out, although she suspected the truth was that he
fascinated her.

'I worked on Wall Street for a similar investment
house.'

'New York?' Her brows shot up.

'I moved there when I was sixteen,' he drawled.

'Which investment house did you work for?'

The black lashes flickered. He gave a hard smile,
and said, 'The only one that I knew could fulfil my
ambition to be a multimillionaire before I was thirty.'

'I take it you succeeded,' she said. 'And developed
even loftier ambitions!'

He laughed sardonically. 'Quite so.'

'Think you'll achieve them, Damian?' she asked
softly, hating him.

'Of course,' he murmured, watching her through
hooded lids. 'I always get what I want, no matter how
hard I have to fight for it.'

A *frisson* of alarm went through her. The respect
that was growing so unstoppably in her heart and mind
told her he not only meant what he said but had proven
beyond doubt that he was capable of it. She felt hurt
and angry and insignificant—did he really see nothing
when he looked at her but the acquisition of Swift?

'And what I want right now,' said Damian, 'is to ask
you a few personal questions.'

She tensed, her smile bitter. 'Ask away!'

He studied her with narrowed eyes. 'Why haven't
you married?'

'Why. . .?' Her hand shook as she replaced her
coffee-cup.

'You're young,' he said coolly, 'beautiful, sexy and
intelligent. You certainly enjoy lovemaking.' The blue

eyes glittered mockingly as he saw the fierce colour rush up her face. 'So why hasn't a man caught you?'

Rachel looked away across the sunlit tree-lined street below. Her heart was beating a slow, hard rhythm. 'I can't stand possessive man,' she said suddenly, 'men who won't let go of me, let me be myself, let me be free. And they're always the kind that marry young, aren't they?'

His eyes narrowed. 'You don't plan to marry Radcliffe?'

She laughed and did not reply, staring out at the trees.

Damian's mouth hardened. He said, 'The idea of marriage makes you feel trapped, then?'

'Very.' She looked back at him. 'How about you? You're hardly in a position to preach the virtues — why haven't you married?'

He gave a sardonic smile. 'Similar reasons.'

Rachel's eyes were scornful. 'Are you serious?'

'Of course.' He shrugged broad shoulders. 'I'm an eligible man. I've had my share of female spiders, spinning webs.'

She felt a stab of jealousy and smiled to cover it. 'But you've never been caught. . .'

'Apparently not,' he drawled.

'Don't like spiders?' Her eyes were very green.

'No,' he drawled. 'Some women approach marriage the way others approach a career. Strategy, game plans, plotting. They'll do anything to make you dependent on them, and then they drag you to the altar and call it love.' His eyes narrowed. 'But it's not love, it's just a long series of tactics.'

'But, as a businessman, surely you'd respect that?'

'In business, sure,' he said coolly, and arched black brows. 'But in my personal life. . .?' He shook his dark

head. 'I do the hunting, thanks very much. Not the
other way around.'

Rachel shivered. He was a hunter all right. Like that
lion, its fierce eyes similar to Damian's. She could just
imagine him closing in for the kill.

The rest of the afternoon was tainted with that
powerful awareness, and as they drove through the city
Rachel was on edge, aware of the predator at her side.

As the sun began to set over Auckland they took a
short flight on a tiny seaplane, and the gold light
enhanced the aerial view of Auckland as the lights
began to come on in white wood houses, skyscrapers,
hotels.

'I can see the shadow of the plane on the water,'
Rachel said with delight, looking out of the window.

'I can't,' said Damian in the cramped interior beside
her, then moved to look out of her window, his body
pressing against hers, one powerful arm across her, his
hard chest against her breasts.

Rachel stared fixedly at his tanned throat where the
white shirt was unbuttoned. Her heart was beating fast.
Damian turned his dark head to look down at her, and
her gaze lifted to his mouth.

'Enjoying our little journey?' he asked under his
breath.

Rachel looked into those powerful dark eyes. 'I'm
hating every minute of it!' she said in a shaking voice,
and then the plane veered sharply to the right and
Damian moved away from her.

When they got back to the hotel, Damian strode
through the foyer, saying curtly, 'I'd like to go over the
minutes you took at the board meeting yesterday.'

She nodded jerkily. 'I still have them. When do you
want them?'

'Tonight.' He got into the lift, his face hard and

unreadable as he jabbed the button for their floor. 'I'll knock for you at eight for dinner. Have them with you.'

That night, she bathed and scented her body in the bath, then blow-dried her hair and applied make-up with great care. She chose a short black lace suit, tight-fitted with a scoop neckline. It was, unfortunately, riotously sexy. But so, unfortunately, were almost all her clothes. Rachel had always enjoyed being a woman, and delighted in her femininity, her sex appeal, the differences that made her so intensely female. Until now, she had met no backlash from her penchant for dressing with unerring sensuality.

But then she had never met a man like Damian Flint before; a man who was as masculine as she was feminine. Perhaps it was inevitable that an attraction should have blazed between them from the first.

When he knocked at her door, she was ready, and opened it with a cool expression.

'Got the minutes?' Damian stood in the doorway, hands thrust in the pockets of a very dark blue suit, immaculately cool, his dark red silk tie and white shirt enhancing the deep tan of his handsome face. He looked so handsome that she felt sick with nerves, weak with attraction.

'Here.' Rachel handed them to him, and he put them in his inside jacket pocket.

They had dinner at a jazz club in the next street. It was a cool night, but the city was alive, and the club was warm, casual, relaxed. A jazz band played on a little stage at the end of the wide, luxurious room, and diners sat and listened at tables covered in white linen and silver.

People began to dance as the female vocalist crooned smoky blues into the microphone, almost kissing it.

' "Fever". . .' Damian drawled. 'One of my favourite songs.'

Rachel watched him through her lashes. 'I like it, too.'

'Does Radcliffe give you fever?' he asked without warning.

Her face flamed. 'Tony is an old friend!'

'You see him every night,' he drawled. 'There must be more between you than memory lane.'

'We like each other,' she said tightly.

'How much?'

'That,' she said with an angry smile, 'is still none of your business!'

His eyes glittered. 'Is he a good lover?'

'Is Domino?' she flashed back furiously, her face flaming.

He laughed under his breath. 'Forget her. Let's go and dance. . .!'

Rachel allowed him to lead her to the dance-floor, but his callous dismissal of the unfortunate Domino was symptomatic of the kind of man he was. As he turned her on the dance-floor and slid his arms around her waist, a shudder of convulsive desire went through her body, and he bent his head, mouth hot against her shivering throat, to whisper thickly, 'I love the way you move. Do you find me a particularly inspiring partner?'

'Far from it!' she said thickly, but her racing pulses told him a different story, and she knew her desire for him was growing stronger with each moment they spent together. So were her feelings. Desire was easy to slam the door on, but emotions were a very different matter, and her fear was beginning to take on new dimensions as she realised Damian Flint threatened her heart even more than he threatened her body.

They walked back to the hotel. When they were

riding up in the lift, Damian said, 'I think we should go over the minutes together.'

'OK.' She shrugged. 'Over breakfast?'

'No, Rachel. Now. In my room.'

Her heart began to beat faster. 'I am not coming to your room!'

'Come on!' he said curtly. 'Try to be professional about this!'

'Professional?' Her eyes flared at the stinging insult, only too aware that he outstripped her professionally. 'You know as well as I do that you want me to come to your room so you can make love to me!'

'I can't be bothered tonight,' he said unpleasantly. 'You're too much trouble.'

She was silent, furious, angry, hurt.

'But we have a hectic business schedule tomorrow,' he drawled as the lift doors slid open. 'And business comes before pleasure.' He strode to his room. 'Come along, Miss Swift. Earn your secretary's pay! That's what you're here for, isn't it?'

Rachel hung back, flushed and unsteady. 'Can't we discuss it elsewhere? In the bar downstairs, or —'

'It's too confidential for public discussion.' He thrust open his bedroom door, turned, hands in the pockets of that immaculate dark blue suit. 'Come on. Inside.'

Slowly, she walked towards him, struggling to quell the alarm bells that were ringing inside her head, and she should have listened to them because the minute she was inside the room Damian closed the door behind him and double-locked it. As she stared at him, she knew it had come, the moment of physical and emotional confrontation she had held off for so long, and she felt so vulnerable that she could barely breathe.

'What are you doing. . .?' she demanded, trying to

sound strong, but her voice was filled with her heart-beat and her vulnerability.

'Come here!' Damian said thickly, and strode towards her, 'My God, I'm just going to throw you on the bloody bed and ——'

'No!' She backed at a rate of knots, her heart slamming.

'I am sick to death of fighting this!' he bit out, reaching for her.

'Get away from me!' Panicked, she threw a chair clumsily at him. 'I said get away!'

There was a brief, tense silence as the chair hit him and he stepped backwards, swearing under his breath.

Rachel said, 'And stay away. . .!' Her voice tailed off.

He looked down at the chair. Then he looked up and bit out thickly, 'The hell I will!' He kicked the chair aside with a violence that sent it crashing across the floor.

She gasped, and whispered something incoherently, her body shaking.

Suddenly, his hand shot out, grabbed her wrist, flicked her against his hard body, and as she gave a hoarse groan of fierce excitement he looked down at her, breathing hard.

'Fight me now, Rachel!' he bit out thickly. 'Fight me now!' And his head swooped, his mouth meeting hers as she moaned, her mouth opening hungrily beneath his, unable to fight now that she was in his arms. The blood was racing through her veins as she kissed him, her hands going blindly to his neck, running through his hair with wild abandon.

He lifted her in his arms, his mouth still on hers with that fierce hot exploration as he carried her to the bed, slid her down on it, joined her. Dazed, overwhelmed with the need and intensity that had sizzled between them since they first met, Rachel did less than resist; she actively acquiesced, arching her body against his as he slid on to the bed on top of her, and his hoarsely muttered words were bitter-sweet to her ears as he renewed the kiss, his heart thudding above her as his hands began to stroke and explore her passionately responsive body.

Rachel heard someone moaning with pleasure and realised it was her. Her mind had gone, just left her. She knew someone's shaking hands were on Damian's tie, pulling it loose, pushing his dark blue jacket to the floor, but they couldn't be her hands — she wouldn't do such a thing; and as their hoarse breathing mingled further she realised his shirt was completely unbuttoned and that she was staring at his bare chest and it was exactly as she had known it would be.

Her shaking hands slid over the tanned flesh. She was breathing raggedly, whispering unintelligible words like someone fevered, delirious.

'Yes. . .touch me. . .!' Damian said thickly, then his mouth was back on hers, he was shouldering out of his shirt. Rachel moved her hands over his bare shoulders, kissed his chest, buried her hot face in the black hairs there. Damian pulled her head back up, groaning, and his mouth reclaimed hers, pushing her backwards on the pillows. Suddenly, as his hands closed over her breasts, she realised that the black lace jacket of her suit was somehow unbuttoned and he was tugging down the lacy bra cups, whispering hotly against her naked throat, and as his head moved lower and his mouth closed hotly over her erect nipples she twisted beneath him, moaning, clutching his dark head as she felt his teeth graze her with agonising pleasure.

'Oh, God!' someone said, and it was him, his voice

thick with excitement. He shifted on her, and she felt
the hard thrust of his manhood against her thigh. 'Yes
. . .yes. . .!' He was pushing her skirt up, sweat on his
tanned forehead as he slid one hand underneath her,
cupping her rear while his mouth claimed hers hungrily.
'Rachel!' he said shakingly as he kissed her. 'I want
you like hell. . .it's driving me mad. . .' His strong
hands fondled her rear, his heart was thudding
furiously. 'Let me take you. . .let me. . .'

Rachel's mind flew back to her like lightning. This
had gone too far, and now that she was in very grave
danger her mind was able to overpower her desire.

'No. . .!' she tried to say against that forceful mouth,
but he either didn't hear, or didn't want to hear. His
hand was pushing her skirt higher, and she panicked.
'No! I said no!' she screamed, slapping at his hand
blindly as she finally managed to drag her bruised
mouth from his.

His dark head jerked back. He stared at her for a
second in stunned silence, breathing hard, his eyes
dazed. Then he said thickly, 'I won't let you down,
Rachel. I'm as good at this as I am at being chairman
of the board — and you know how good I am at that. . .'
He stared down at her semi-nude body. 'God. . . I
want you so much I'm in pain. . .'

'Go to hell!' she burst out hoarsely and started to
fight in deadly earnest, slapping and scratching at him,
little cries of panic coming from the back of her throat
as her mind flashed back into full operation and she
realised with sick fear just how close she had come to
the edge.

'All right!' he bit out harshly, suddenly, taking her
wrists and pinning them to the bed, breathing raggedly.
'All right. . . I'm not going to rape you!'

'Let me go!'

'No,' he said thickly. 'Tell me what changed your mind! You were ready to let me take you a minute ago; now what the hell happened?'

Shame flooded her, and she said fiercely, 'I know what you're trying to do! You want to seduce me so you can get your hands on the company!'

'Oh, for God's sake! Not the bloody company again! Stop throwing that at me! The company's the very last thing I want to get my hands on right now, and you know it!'

'Don't lie!' she said bitterly, deeply hurt by his endless obsession with power because it attacked the very roots of her growing feelings for him. 'I know all about your plans to marry me and get the company.'

There was a brief, tense silence. He studied her with glittering eyes, his face darkly flushed.

'All right,' he said under his breath. 'Since you've brought it up, let's get down to brass tacks! Marrying me is a *fait accompli*! There's no way out for either of us — not if we're both going to get what we want!'

'And what do I get out of it?'

'Your father's life?' he suggested bitingly.

'There must be another way!'

'Come on, then! Shatter me! What's the other option?'

She looked away, eyes stinging. 'All right, there isn't another option! I have to marry you because if I don't my father could die!'

'Precisely. Not only could he die, but you could inherit and hand the whole thing over to Jamie, which will ultimately make you heiress to nothing but tragedy, bankruptcy and disaster!' He drew a rough breath. 'So don't lie to yourself or to me, Rachel. Our marriage has been on the cards from day one, and there's not a damned thing either of us can do about it.'

Tears blurred her vision. She looked at him, mouth trembling. 'Only because you want the company!'

'And you want your father to live,' he drawled tightly. 'Fair exchange is no robbery. I give you what you want — you give me what I want. Everybody walks away happy.'

'Only we don't walk away separately, do we?' she said under her breath, hating him.

'No, we get the Hollywood sunset!' he drawled sardonically.

'I don't want it!' she flung.

His blue eyes dropped to her mouth. 'Oh, but there is something you do want. . .'

She stiffened in his arms, tried to get away. 'Let me go!'

'I've wanted to make love to you since I first set eyes on you.'

'Let me go!' Her panic was rising.

He held her hard beneath him, said thickly, 'It's mutual — isn't it? If I just wanted you, I'd be able to spend time alone with you without going half crazy. But you want me too, don't you?'

She was breathing raggedly. 'No. . .!'

'Rachel, I'm a man of thirty-three, not an inexperienced boy. I've known a lot of women in my time, and——'

'In the Biblical sense, no doubt!'

'Don't fight me out of pride or anger. We have to marry, but this is separate, this is something quite different, and I want you like hell, Rachel, I want you to give me everything you've got. . .' He lowered his dark head, his mouth claiming hers in a fierce, hot kiss as his hand stroked her breast, sending shock waves of pleasure through her. 'Give it to me. . .' he said thickly against her mouth as she struggled. 'Don't fight, don't struggle. . .just give as you did a minute ago. . .!'

'Go to hell!' she whispered bitterly against his mouth, and when he refused to stop she bit hard into his lower lip.

He jerked his head back, blood on his mouth, stared down at her in fury for a second, then said tightly, 'You little bitch! I may not be able to make you admit you want me, but I can certainly make your body admit it, and I damned well will!'

'Get off me!' She fought bitterly as he came back to her.

He pinned her arms at her sides, eyes blazing. 'I want you and I'll have you! Why the hell shouldn't I? Radcliffe and half his friends have!'

It was like a slap in the face, the insult so unexpected, and the revelation of what he had really thought of her all along was so hurtful, so callous that she went rigid in his arms, white with stiff dignity, eyes brilliant with pain. There it was, out in the open, the reality of what he thought of her. She wanted to die. . .

Damian's black lashes flickered. He had read the expression on her face correctly, and it made him pause, uncertain suddenly.

'Well, haven't they?' his deep voice asked.

Tears stung her green eyes. 'Yes. Of course. I'm a whore. Is that what you want to hear?' Her voice was fragmented like broken glass, her face icy white.

He stared at her and as she met his shocked gaze she felt tears squeeze out over her lashes with hot, blinding intensity.

'I thought ——' he began.

'I can see what you thought!'

There was another tense silence.

'It was just an opinion I formed,' Damian said

thickly, staring at her. 'You kept hanging around with Radcliffe and his crowd. All those young men who thought you were so sexy. . .'

'Please let me go!' she said hoarsely, trying to cover her face with her hands. She felt broken.

He stared into her face. 'Are you trying to tell me you didn't sleep with any of them?'

'Let me go!' She jerked her face from him, struggling.

His hand caught her chin, forced her to look at him. 'Answer my question, damn you!' he said under his breath. 'Did you sleep with Radcliffe or any of his friends?'

She looked at him, her mouth shaking and her eyes blazing with pain, and shouted hoarsely, 'No!'

'Not one of them?' he whispered.

'Not one!' The tears were slipping down her cheeks. Damian Flint, the man she admired so much, thought she was some cheap little floozy he could get into bed while taking Swift at the same time. What a compliment. What a life's work.

His face was rigid. 'Don't tell me you're a virgin!' he said suddenly. 'Don't tell me that. . .'

'Why not?' she demanded bitterly. 'Will it make you feel like the swine you are?'

He drew a harsh breath, muttered something under his breath, then looked away and released her, getting off the bed in those dark blue trousers, his chest bare, thrusting his hands into his pockets, his back to her while she sat up and fumbled to rearrange her clothes, tears falling silently over her cheeks.

The silence dragged on.

Suddenly, Damian said thickly, 'The night I came to your flat in London, you fell into the door with

Radcliffe. I heard him say he was your demon lover. I thought——'

'You've made it very clear what you thought!'

'It was an easy mistake to make.' He raked a hand through his black hair, turning to look at her with very dark eyes. 'Everything you said and did made me think you were a very experienced woman.'

She winced, buttoning up her black lace jacket.

'I didn't put that very well,' he drawled wryly, watching her.

She flashed her eyes up at him, hatred in their depths. 'Oh, I think you put it very succinctly indeed.' Tugging her black lace skirt down, she stood up, still trembling, and snatched up her small black handbag from the floor.

'Look.' Damian walked to her. 'I can see you're very upset, but I did ask you this morning—remember? I knew there was something odd about the way you kissed me, and——'

'I'm not interested!' she said tightly, turning to walk away.

He caught her wrist. 'I said I thought you were uninhibited but strangely naïve. You didn't answer. I took that to be answer enough. That you were experienced. That you had been to bed with all those——'

'Oh, for God's sake!' she shouted suddenly, eyes blazing. 'Are you trying to make this even more intolerable for me than it already is?'

His face tightened. He stepped out of her way and she took a deep breath as she ran to the door and slammed it shut behind her.

In her own room, she doubled-locked the door then stumbled to the bed, sinking down on it, her face white. Devastated. . .he's completely smashed me to bits, she thought, just as I knew he would.

She felt almost traumatised by the revelation of just how much she really did want him to make love to her combined with his ruthless words about marriage, then his callous statements about what a loose little floozy he thought she was—and his finally saying it straight out: 'Don't tell me you're a virgin!' with horror in his eyes.

Numb with agony and humiliation, she got undressed like a ghost and went to bed, unable to let herself dwell too deeply on what had happened in case she found herself asking the inevitable question: if I hate Damian Flint, why has he been able to hurt me so deeply?

Next morning she woke from an intense dream, and did not dare wonder about its meaning. She also did not know how to face Damian. He knew too much about her now. She couldn't pretend to be sophisticated and flippant and terribly cool any more. He would just look at her with those piercing eyes and make her feel as vulnerable as she was beginning to realise she was. How could she hide that? How. . .?

At seven forty-five, she was dressed and ready to face him over breakfast, but a knock on the door made her stiffen.

'Who is it?' she called, staring at the door.

'Damian,' his deep voice said. 'Let me in. I need to talk to you.'

Rachel's stomach churned. 'You must be joking! After last night——'

'I'm not going to seduce you,' he cut in flatly. 'Just open the door and let me in. We have to talk before we leave for the office.'

Something in the tone of his voice reached her and she found herself unlocking the door, opening it, looking up at his hard, handsome face with wary eyes.

'Thank you.' He strode coolly into the bedroom,

chairman of the board once more in an impeccable grey suit.

Rachel closed the door and stayed close to it. 'Well?'

He turned to face her. 'It's time we got this marraige question settled. We discussed the whole thing last night in my room, but we didn't reach a final conclusion, and today we have to.'

'Can't it wait till we get back?'

'No,' he said flatly.

'But I don't want to discuss it!'

'I'm afraid you must. Your father fully expects us to marry in a matter of weeks, and so do I.'

'What. . .?' She stared, her face white. 'But — but I'm not ready! I need time to think, to try to come to terms with —'

'You've had all the time I can give,' he said tightly. 'Now I need your answer before we fly back to Hong Kong tonight. Will you marry me — yes or no?'

CHAPTER SEVEN

DAMIAN stood against the sunlight flooding in through the windows, his hands thrust in his grey trouser pockets, the silver watch-chain across his powerful chest reflecting light.

'I had planned to propose last night,' he said, watching her stricken face. 'But if you remember. . .nothing went according to plan. Now I don't have much time left. It's rushed, I know, but at least you have a day to think it over before we fly—'

'I'd die rather than marry you!' Rachel broke out shakingly, her lips white.

'Unfortunately, it's your father, not you, who will die if you don't.'

'Don't throw that at me, you bastard!' she burst out hoarsely. 'Do you think I don't know how ill he is?'

'I know you don't,' he said tightly. 'If you did, you would already be my wife.'

'But he can't be in such immediate danger, or—'

'This isn't his first attack,' Damian cut in harshly.

There was a little silence. She was aware of the light flooding in coldly, shafts of sunlight with little dust particles in them.

'We didn't tell you because it wasn't serious,' Damian said, 'just a mild flutter at first, nothing too unusual in a man of his age.'

'When was this?' she whispered, appalled.

'Just after you left for England. It all coincided at that point. His fears for the future, his growing worry about you — and that rapidly shrinking cage of hatred he shares with Jamie.'

'But how do you know all this?' she asked shakily. 'You didn't even start working for him until——'

'Just after you left for England,' he said flatly. 'I was with him when he had his third mild heart attack.'

'His third!' Her face was white. 'Oh, God. . .'

'That's when it all came pouring out. His fears about you, Jamie, the company. I could see at once he was working himself into a panic about it all. I could also see there was no solution. Not with that clause in your grandfather's will.'

Her eyes widened. 'You know about that. . .!' It was the final straw; she could see he knew everything, everything, and that took away every last hidden ace she had ever hoped to possess.

'That clause is the lynchpin on which his heart attacks have revolved, Rachel,' he said flatly. 'I know how fond you are of your uncle, but even you must see what would happen if he was left holding the reins.'

She looked at him bitterly. 'Jamie is a nice man! He's kind and loving and he deserves better than that condemnation! He's just had a rough deal, that's all.'

'Give me a break!' he drawled unpleasantly. 'We all have to play with the hand we're dealt, and up to a certain point we can put the blame on the dealer, but that point passed for Jamie Swift thirty years ago.' His mouth was a hard, ruthless line. 'He's thrown his life away, and he'd throw the company away if he was given it.'

Rachel couldn't deny that. Much as she loved Jamie and hated Damian, she couldn't deny it.

'That leaves you and me,' Damian said coolly, watching her. 'If we marry immediately, we can save everything.'

The worst part was that they both knew she had to say yes. Would he expect her to sleep in his bed, make love to him? Her heart thudded like a sledge-hammer. Who was she kidding? After last night? Of course he would! What else would he expect? Nothing, probably. Nothing at all because that was what he felt for her.

'And what do you get out of all of this?' she asked in a shaking voice. 'Or need I ask?'

'You can ask,' he said expressionlessly. 'And I'll tell you. I get a great deal, as we both know. In the first place, I'm fond of your father and would genuinely like to keep him away from that fatal heart attack. In the second place—naturally, I want Swift Investments——'

'Naturally!'

'There's nothing wrong with ambition.'

'There is when it tramples on other people's lives!'

'This marriage won't trample on your life,' he said curtly. 'On the contrary—it can only enhance it. You told me yesterday that you hated the idea of marriage because you couldn't stand jealous, possessive men.'

She winced, looking away.

'Jealousy is a symptom of love,' Damian went on, shattering her further as she remembered her own jealousy. 'I won't be a jealous, possessive husband for the simple reason that I'm not in love with you.'

Stung, she retorted, 'Good! Because I'm not in love with you, either!'

A muscle jerked in his cheek. 'Then I don't see the problem.'

She suddenly wanted to throw something at him, anything, needing to hurt him as she was hurting, but couldn't actually reach his ambitious heart, so she aimed for the next best thing: his self-respect. 'You say you're not going to be jealous or possessive. Does that mean I can see other men? Tony? His friends?'

He gave a harsh laugh. 'No way! I'll have no other men near you, in public or in private! I'm counting on you to give me children, and I won't have a slur on their legitimacy.'

Her eyes blazed. 'How dare you even suggest that? How dare you? After what I told you last night, I——'

'What you told me last night, Rachel, only convinced me that this marriage could work,' he said softly, and walked towards her with a look of intent in his blue eyes that sent panic rushing through her in hot waves.

She backed against the door. 'Don't come near me!'

'You're a virgin and I've woken you up!' he drawled, reaching her, strong hands sliding to her waist. 'That makes me feel peachy-keen, but I'd like you to be a little more specific about your innocence.' He held her hard against the door, his dark face very close. 'How far have you gone in the past with Radcliffe. . .and the others? As far as we went last night? Or even further?'

'Oh, God. . .!' she choked out thickly, pushing at his shoulders, but he was so strong that she was helpless against that strength, her heart pounding as she felt his hard thighs press closer against her to trap her there.

'Well?' His eyes narrowed, he thrust her chin up with one hard hand. 'Answer me!'

'It's none of your business!' she said hoarsely.

'Tell me, Rachel,' he said thickly, 'or I'll start making love to you and I won't stop until I get the truth out of you! And we both know just how much I'd like to carry on doing it, so don't tempt me to start!'

Her face burned. She lowered her lashes, said bitterly, 'I—I've never gone as far as I did last night with you!'

She could hear his heart beating rapidly against his

powerful chest. Or was it her heart? The blood was
racing round her veins as she felt the evidence of his
fierce excitement hard against her.

'I see,' he said thickly, staring fixedly down at her.

Rachel couldn't look up to meet his eyes. 'Will you
let me go now?'

'I don't think so.' He laughed under his breath.

There was another silence, pulsing with desire, and
Rachel was staring at his chest, her hands curling on
his shoulders, scarcely able to move as her emotions
were swept ruthlessly aside by her physical desire for
him. This would be the pattern of their marriage. She'd
be hurt, angry, filled with hatred. . .but he'd only have
to touch her to have her dizzy with excitement in his
arms again. She despised herself. She wanted him to
kiss her. She wanted what happened last night to
happen again, right now, here in her own bedroom. . .

Suddenly, she whispered, 'I don't want to marry
you!'

'You don't want to marry me——' his hot mouth was
less than an inch above her face as she stared resolutely
at his dark red silk tie '—but there's something else
you do want to do with me.'

'No. . .!' It was her Achilles' heel and he knew it.

'I'd take your clothes off now and prove it to you,'
he said thickly, and his hands were shaking as they
held her by the hips. 'But, in the circumstances, I feel
I must wait until we're married before I do that.'

She closed her eyes, head spinning, mouth dry, and
felt her hands curl helplessly with desire on his broad
shoulders.

'It's rare,' Damian said under his breath, 'but we've
got it, and it'll make everything else easier to deal
with.'

Her eyes flew suddenly to his. 'What do you mean,

it's rare? You must have had hundreds of mistresses all over the world——'

'I've never had any problem getting women into bed, it's true,' he drawled, 'But I've rarely felt a mutual attraction as intense as the one we share. We must score a ring-a-ding-ding one hundred per cent on the sexual compatibility rating!'

'That's not enough to build a marriage on!'

'What we have isn't love, but at least it isn't a cold professional relationship.'

His words knifed into her. 'Some compensation!' she flung. 'I wanted love!'

'I can't give it to you,' he drawled tightly.

She almost flinched, but somehow her pride rescued her from that, although she felt as though he'd stuck a knife in her heart and started to revolve it.

'We all have to give up our dreams some time, Rachel,' Damian said.

'Not you, though,' she whispered bitterly. 'You get everything you wanted, don't you? The company, the money, the girl. . .'

He nodded, his face ruthless, and said, 'We'll announce the news to your father as soon as we return!'

Of course, her father was over the moon.

'I'm so pleased!' he said, clutching her in a clumsy embrace. 'This is what I've dreamt of for so long. . .' He released her, turned to Damian, shook his hand vigorously. 'Didn't I tell you you'd fall in love with her at first sight?'

'And you were right,' drawled Damian with a sardonic glance at Rachel. 'I wanted her the minute I set eyes on her.'

Her eyes flared angrily. She knew his true meaning only too well.

'When will you marry?' Charles asked.

'Three weeks from now,' Damian said. 'It'll give everyone time to get ready for the wedding itself.'

'That's the middle of August,' Charles observed. 'Yes, that should be time enough. Let me see — what does one need for a wedding? The dress, the invitations, the reception party, catering, flowers. . .oh, lord!' He was flushed with excitement. 'What a lot there is to do! Let's open the champagne and celebrate! Nightingale. . .!'

Rachel allowed herself to be swept along in her father's excitement, drinking champagne on the sunlit, steamy terrace with him and seeing the difference in his face and demeanour as the news gradually sank in.

How could she regret her decision where he was concerned? He looked as though he'd lost twenty years, as though a ten-ton weight had been lifted from his shoulders. She thought of those other, milder heart attacks and felt afraid for him.

Later, she and Damian drove down into Central District to buy her engagement ring. They went to Cartier's in the Landmark, the black and gold shopping mall for the extremely wealthy. Damian chose a huge square-cut emerald set in platinum that flashed like green fire against her finger. She almost fainted at the price.

'I want you to dine with me tomorrow night,' Damian said as they left Cartier's and strolled along the marble corridors. 'At my villa.'

Rachel shot him a sharp look. 'Your villa?'

'Don't look so alarmed,' he drawled under his breath. 'I told you, I won't take you until our wedding night.'

Her heart beat raggedly. 'How do I know I can trust you? If we're alone in your villa——'

'I just want you to see it,' he said coolly. 'You'll be moving in there once we're married, and it'll give you a chance to look around.'

The reality of the forthcoming wedding was becoming intolerable. Rachel was pale as she walked beside him into the cool marble courtyard, the towering stone fountain echoing beneath the glass dome.

'Iced tea?' Damian said, glancing up at one of the balcony cafés.

Rachel moistened dry lips. 'Why not?'

They took the escalator up and settled at a table overlooking the fountain. People were everywhere. Rich women with Chanel bags rested their weary shopping feet and met their friends for a drink.

'Thought about the guest list?' Damian asked coolly.

She looked up. 'Jamie must be invited.'

He inclined his dark head, mouth hard. 'You realise he hates me every bit as much as he hates your father?'

'He's my uncle,' she said tightly. 'I won't exclude him.'

'I didn't ask you to,' he said expressionlessly. 'I just think you should remember how *he* feels. This wedding is what he's been afraid of. He might very well —— ' He broke off suddenly, blue eyes shooting past her.

Rachel turned instinctively to glance round. Her eyes lit up. 'Tony!'

'Wo!' Tony was right behind her and bent his blond head to kiss her smiling mouth. 'How are you, trendy young babe?'

Rachel kissed him back. 'Funkadelic, trendy young dude!'

They both laughed, eyes shining, faces close.

'Hi, Damian!' Tony smiled, then did a double-take at the look in Damian's knife-like eyes. 'I — I mean Mr

Flint!' he amended hurriedly and extended a hand. 'How are you, sir?'

Damian studied the extended hand with icy distate, then flicked his hardened blue eyes to Rachel. 'We have to leave. Are you ready?'

'But I'd like to talk to——' she began angrily, resenting his attitude.

'Good day to you, Radcliffe!' Damian said bitingly, and got to his feet, thrusting a handful of Hong Kong dollars on to the table. 'Come along, Rachel!'

Her eyes warred bitterly with his, but she had no choice. She got to her feet too, turning to Tony. 'I'll ring you later and explain.'

Damian's hand caught her wrist in a biting grip. 'Rachel!'

'A group of us are going down to 1997 tonight!' Tony called after her as she was dragged away by Damian. 'We'll be there till midnight!'

Rachel was furious, scurrying after her tall, arrogant fiancé, her wrist in his hard hand as he strode across the marble floors with a set face towards the exit on Des Voeux Road.

'How dare you behave like that?' Rachel stormed as they emerged into the hot glare of the sun, people everywhere, shoe-shiners on the corners and street pedlars shouting against the rattle of the green trams.

'You're my fiancée!' he said bitingly. 'My future wife! I will not have you kissing other men in public! As for his invitation—if I catch you at 1997 with him or any other man, I'll revoke my decision about the wedding night, and take you to bed immediately!' He lifted a strong hand, signalled brusquely for the Mercedes to pick them up, and pushed her into the rear seats, sliding in next to her.

'I thought you weren't jealous and possessive!' she said shakingly as they drove off into the traffic.

'I'm not,' he said tightly.

'Then what was all that about?'

'In case you've forgotten,' he said, eyes flashing, 'you are wearing my ring and an announcement is appearing in the South China *Morning Post* tomorrow morning. We are now publicly engaged. If you kiss another man publicly, or go out with him to a nightclub like 1997, you'll humiliate me in front of the whole damned colony!'

'Tony's one of my oldest friends! We were at school together! Nobody's going to think anything's going on between us!'

'I thought something was between you,' he said tightly. 'I still do.'

'You mean you don't believe what I told you in Auckland?' Her eyes flared. 'Oh, that just about takes the——'

'Rachel,' he said bitingly, 'you're not to see him again!'

She stared, face white. 'Not ever?'

He met her gaze, his face hard and obdurate and determined.

'You can't be serious!' she said, although she could see by the look on his face that he was deadly serious. 'For God's sake, Damian! I've know Tony almost all my life!'

'Start a new life,' he said flatly. 'Without him.'

Her eyes flared with searing jealousy and frustrated rage. 'Not unless you do the same with Domino Mei-Ling!'

There was a brief silence. The car swung up towards Repulse Bay, the cliffs bleached dusty beige, a shanty town on the right, made of metal slates in a deserted patch of land.

'You won't, will you?' Rachel said, jealousy revolving like a knife in her heart. 'You'll make me stop seeing my oldest friend, but you won't let your mistress go!'

He looked at her, eyes veiled by hooded lids. 'I'm a little more discreet, Rachel.'

She caught her breath, appalled by the pain and jealousy she felt. 'My God. . .you're going to carry on sleeping with her. . .aren't you?' Her voice shook. 'Aren't you?'

Damian's mouth twisted in a hard smile. 'What I do regarding Domino is my business.'

'Why, you——' she began in a shaking voice.

'What you do with young Radcliffe, however,' he cut in harshly, 'could blow the whistle on us all! The minute our engagement is announced the gossip-mongers in this little hotbed of a colony will be ready to pounce on any evidence that this is—as they have long predicted—a marriage of convenience!'

'Well, isn't that what it is?' she said hoarsely, hating him.

'I don't want to be the subject of vicious gossip!' he said bitingly. 'And if you make me one, Rachel, I warn you—I'll teach you a lesson you'll never forget!' His eyes swept her body with implicit meaning. 'Not as long as you live!'

Rachel sat there in the back of the Mercedes, unable to give him the stinging retort on her lips because she knew he would do what he promised, and she had a profound fear that the minute he made love to her fully the feelings she was desperately trying to suppress would keel over and completely overwhelm her, leaving her not just vulnerable but absolutely devastated by the reality of what they were. She kept trying to trample them, slam the door, but he kept kicking it back open and sooner or later she'd have to put a name to her feelings, and she was afraid, so afraid, that the name was love. . .but it mustn't be, she thought savagely; it can't be. I won't let it be.

That night, she went to see Jamie at his apartment on Tai Hang Road.

'I've agreed to marry Damian Flint. . .'

Jamie turned his handsome face from her, a bleak look entering his blue eyes. In the silence, she heard a cockatoo singing in the jacaranda trees outside, the fringed green leaves wafting in the humid breeze.

'Jamie——' she touched his strong shoulder '—please don't take it too badly. I had no real choice. In the end, it was the only possible——'

'I know, I know!' he said tightly, waving a hand to shut her up. Then he gave a harsh sigh. 'I guess I've had long enough to accept it. I knew as soon as he entered the company. I knew this would happen. . .'

'Father's going to put another clause in the will,' she said rapidly. 'Leaving you a substantial sum of money—millions, probably—and a new position. Director of customer entertainments for the Far East.'

'Customer entertainments!' he said bitterly. 'Adding insult to bloody injury!'

'Jamie, don't take it that way,' she said with a heartfelt sigh. 'I know you're hurt and disappointed, but this is a good opportunity. Don't you see? You can end all this hatred and enmity. Just put it behind you forever. Start a new life, live for new things. Positive things; not the dark, destructive forces that have damaged your life for so long.'

He looked at her with those bleak eyes.

'This is the end, Jamie,' she said gently. 'It's all over

now. I must marry Damian, and he will get the
company when my father dies.'

He nodded, his mouth a bitter line, but she could
see acceptance in the way he bowed his dark head, and
she felt deep compassion for him, for his wasted life
and wasted efforts and wasted pain.

When she got home, she felt sad and empty, thinking
of her uncle. If only there was something she could do
to help him cope. With her marriage to Damian, his
life's work of fighting Charles for the company was
finally at an end. He had nothing to live for. How
would he manage to be happy?

Rachel flopped exhausted into the long white sofa
and wrote a long letter to Jenny, pouring her heart out
for the first time in three weeks, telling her everything
that had happened since she left. All she omitted were
her feelings for Damian, because they were too private,
too intense and too confusing. And they were growing
faster than ever before. . .

The next evening, she had dinner with Damian at his
villa.

'The boy next door!' she commented bitterly as she
crossed the threshold, tense in a white silk dress.

'The man next door,' he drawled, eyes narrowing as
he closed the front door. 'Or should I say — the chairman next door?'

Rachel walked across the polished floor of the hall,
eyes flickering with surprise over the stone walls, the
Oriental statue eerily lit, guarding the doorway to the
living-room.

The ground floor was vast, sprawling, with four
reception-rooms, a huge mahogany kitchen and the
gym. He had decorated in international taste; she saw
African statues, bronze statues from India, from
Peru — even a tall redwood statue of a Sioux Indian.

The gym was a stark open room with windowed walls and beige carpet. In the living-room, a smoked glass hi-fi dominated the mahogany wall unit, huge speakers beside it. Two couches in the centre of the room faced each other, gleaming dark red leather beneath the lights.

It was beautiful, and somehow the knowledge that she loved his home made her slam that emotional door even more ruthlessly, turning blindly from her true feelings to hate him more.

'What made you buy it,' she asked tightly, 'right next door to my father? Or shall I guess?'

'You know as well as I do that ninety per cent of the population in Hong Kong live in apartments. I wanted a villa,' he drawled. 'This one came up for sale, so I grabbed it. It was either that or some whacking great palace out in the New Territories or one of the outlying islands.'

'I would have thought a whacking great palace more to your taste!'

'Not if I had to face a helicopter journey every time I wanted to come into town,' he drawled, and then slowly lowered his gaze to her red mouth, murmuring, 'So. . .do you want to see the bedrooms?'

Her heart thudded with a fierce violence. 'No!'

He gave a tight smile. 'You'll have to sooner or later.'

'I prefer later!' she said angrily, and turned from him, suffocated by his closeness, that hard body making hers rush with heat.

True to his word, he did not try to seduce her. He didn't even try to kiss her, which was very noticeable, as they spent most of the evening staring at each other, feeling electricity crackle between them every time they accidentally touched, and, by the time Rachel left, her stomach was clenched in a knot of intolerable excitement.

'I'll see you at the office on Monday morning,' Damian told her as he walked her home in the hot, humid night to her own villa next door and cicadas buzzed metallically as they walked past the fountain.

Rachel stopped in the hot shadows beneath the front door, looked up. 'Why? Are you busy tomorrow?' Her eyes flared with jealous pain and she said, twisting the knife into herself, 'Seeing Domino?'

He watched her intently, his body disturbingly close. 'Why — does that bother you?'

'Not in the least!' she said quickly, too quickly, her voice thick.

'Really?' He gave a cool laugh and drawled, 'Well, if I didn't know better, I'd say you sounded jealous!'

All heartbeat ceased. She had to say something fast and make it convincing. 'I'm just angry because you want me to stop seeing Tony! He's my friend and I love him!'

'Too bad!' he bit out thickly, a stain of red on his hard cheekbones.

'Why is it too bad?' she demanded. 'Why do I have to give up Tony when you won't give Domino up?'

His eyes flared with temper. 'I'll give her up once I've taken you to bed, Rachel, and not before!'

Turning on his heel, he strode away, and she watched him bitterly, consumed with pain. Later, she stood alone at her bedroom window, looking out at the moonlit sea. He would be with Domino tomorrow. Would they make love all day at some hot, steamy house somewhere in this glittering cosmopolitan city? Rachel's hands were white-knuckled on the window-sill as she pictured it, vivid images burning into her mind.

She couldn't stand it. The thought of that hard mouth moving over another woman's lips, his hands on her body, his hard thighs parting hers. . .no, no, no! her mind screamed.

Shaking, she turned her back on the sea, stared hectically into her darkened bedroom. The jealousy she felt was escalating out of all control. She felt angry enough to kill.

I won't let him have other women! she thought fiercely. How dare he even consider it? But what could she do, how could she stop him? She felt like running round to his villa right now, in the middle of the night, banging on the door, screaming jealous, incoherent orders at him that she knew he would not obey.

Suddenly, Damian's own words floated back to her: 'I won't be a jealous, possessive husband for the simple reason that I'm not in love with you.' She stood stock-still, thinking, I'm so jealous I can't think straight, but I'm not in love with him, I'm not; I can't be. . .

It explained everything, though she fought it, fought the nightmare truth of her growing feelings for him, her respect, her admiration, her jealousy, her pain, her longing to make him feel something for her, anything, so long as it came from the heart and not the body. . .

Grabbing desperately at any life-raft, she found one: Damian's words again. 'It's rare. . .but we've got it. . . We must score a ring-a-ding-ding one hundred per cent on the sexual compatibility rating!' Relief swamped her. Yes, that was it. That was the explanation for her jealousy; it had to be.

But although her explanation made logical sense — it did not make emotional sense. Suddenly, she remembered someone had once told her that falling in love was a frightening experience.

Her stomach slowly somersaulted. She felt sick. She felt shaky. She felt frightened. She felt every emotion in the book of love but she must not be in love with Damian Flint; she must not, must not, must not. . .

CHAPTER EIGHT

SOMEHOW, Rachel went into the office on Monday morning, smiling as she was politely congratulated by the staff, who admired her ring. The *Morning Post* carried the announcement of their engagement that weekend, but on Monday they printed a small article about the forthcoming wedding. Beneath a photograph of Damian looking very hard and sexy they printed the words, 'Damian Flint — New Chairman of Swift?'

'Very cryptic!' Damian drawled, leaning back with his feet on the desk, studying the newspaper.

'Very accurate!'

'Yes,' he agreed softly, lifting his blue eyes to hers.

She met that mocking gaze angrily, then said with a sick rush of jealousy, 'Enjoy your last moments with Domino?'

'The rest of the colony may have nothing better to do than gossip about my private life, but I draw the line at my fiancée joining in.' He swept her with a commanding gaze, and said flatly, 'Get back to your desk and get on with your work.'

'My work?' she said tightly, hating him. 'We both know I was never really your secretary. That was just an excuse to throw us together so you could seduce me! Shall I even bother to hand my notice in?'

'Go and type it up now!' he drawled tightly. 'You resign as of our wedding day.'

Bitterly, she left with a slam of the door.

Luckily, Domino Mei-Ling did not come into the office to meet Damian for lunch that week. Presumably, he had warned her off. Very sensible, given the gossip that was whirling up around their heads.

But as the week wore on and Damian made no attempt to see her at night, spend time with her or try to kiss her, she realised he was seeing Domino in the dark, humid hours when Rachel sat alone at home, tortured by jealousy, consumed with it, imagining them together and burning with impotent rage. She felt as though he had flung her into hell.

Meanwhile, Charles was recovering in leaps and bounds. He rarely came into the office, spending most of his time with his old friends waxing lyrical about his splendid son-in-law to be.

July turned to August, and the heat was suffocating. Butter melted to liquid in half an hour if left out of the fridge. One day, the rains came, flooding the city in warm, wet torrents. Rachel left the office and ran out on to Des Voeux, hailing a taxi to take her home. The car swept up flooded streets. A rat as big as a cat scurried down a steep slope and a small bush slid down after it in the torrential downpour.

The taxi stopped briefly, and as it did Rachel saw another taxi stopping on the other side of the road. Damian got out, his arm around Domino, and they ran into an apartment block. Rachel sat there, staring after them, her face white as her own taxi pulled away.

Next day when she went into the office she said icily, 'I saw you with her yesterday. I want you to promise me you'll never see her again.'

He tensed at his desk, watching her, suddenly very still. Slowly, he put down the silver pen he had been toying with and stood up, walking to her at the windows.

'Her mother was ill,' he said deeply. 'I promised to pay for——'

'Don't give me that nickle and dime stuff!' she burst out shakingly, her eyes blazing with pain. 'You said you were going to be discreet!'

'I have been discreet,' he said tightly. 'No one saw me with her.'

'*I* saw you!' Her voice shook with emotion. She struggled to control it, fighting for dignity, her body rigid with pride. 'If I saw you, someone else must have done. It'll be all over the colony in no time. I want you to stop seeing her. Now.'

His mouth tightened. 'It's only another week to the wedding.'

'I don't care!' she said in a low, angry voice, 'Stop seeing her now or I'll start seeing Tony. Publicly. Every night at 1997.'

There was a tense silence.

'I'm not taking orders from you, Rachel,' he said under his breath. 'Don't dish them out, or I'll counter-act them in a way you won't like.'

Her pulses thudded with anger. 'Such as?'

'I'll kiss her in front of you,' he drawled tightly. 'That ought to put paid to your demands that I —'

Something snapped inside her and she flew at him, hoarse cries coming from the back of her throat as she slapped and scratched at him until he caught her wrists and dragged her hard against his powerful body.

'Is it jealousy?' he demanded in an odd, hoarse voice. 'If it is, say so! I'll stop seeing her if it's hurting you!'

'Go to hell!' she spat, humiliated beyond endurance, and struggled to get away from him. 'I'm not jealous of you and your sordid little affairs! I just don't want to be humiliated in public!'

His mouth tightened and he released her with a shove, raking a hand through his black hair. 'I'll stop

seeing her once we're married and not before,' he said,
his eyes like knives. 'And I give you my word that I
will not be seen in public again with her.'

'You gave me your word before. . .'

'Rachel!' he bit out. 'Don't push me.!'

The look in his eyes was warning enough. With a
white, set face, she left the office and went straight to
the ladies' powder-room, breaking down in private and
crying silent, bitter tears. She hated herself for backing
down, but what could she do? He had said he would
stop seeing her if Rachel confessed to jealousy, to
being hurt. Never! she thought fiercely. I'd die before
admitting the way I feel. Resolutely, she splashed her
face with icy water, repaired her make-up, and went
back to her desk to face the nightmare with only her
dignity to mask her pain.

On Thursday, Damian's family arrived from Kenya,
and they all went out to dinner with Charles at the
Jumbo floating restaurant in Aberdeen harbour. His
sister Katya and his mother Lydia were both slender,
green-eyed brunettes, and his father, a silver-haired
man with icy blue eyes, barely had a civil word to say
to his successful son. When they boarded the glittering
red, gold and green floating restaurant, the *maître d'*
took them down to the fresh fish display in the base.

'Oh, Damian, look!' Katya, his sister, took his arm,
pointing to the live crabs wriggling and pinching in a
mesh basket.

'Damian, it was so clever of you to bring us here!'
Lydia, his mother, took his other arm.

Rachel walked behind, forgotten and ignored, her
eyes burning with fury. I'm even jealous of his mother
and his sister, she realised, despising herself. Later,
they went upstairs to their table, laid with white linen,

silver chopstick-holders, and hand-painted porcelain crockery.

'Dearest Katya,' said Lydia with a frozen smile, 'is planning on wearing a scarlet dress to the wedding.'

'Scarlet suits me,' Katya purred. 'Don't you think, Damian?'

'Very much so,' he drawled, amused.

'Mother,' said Katya, 'is upset because you didn't like her wedding present.'

'He did like my wedding present!' Lydia snapped. 'Didn't you?'

'Yes, it was beautiful,' Damian said, mouth sardonic, and so it went on, the two women vying for his attention all through dinner as the lights of Aberdeen harbour, on the far side of Hong Kong island, gleamed across the water and night fell.

The next evening, Rachel and Damian unwrapped some more wedding presents together at her father's villa. His family were out to dinner alone together.

'I need the afternoon off tomorrow,' Rachel told him. 'Jenny's arriving from London. I have to meet her at the airport.'

'You can leave after lunch,' he said flatly, and then paused, frowning as he pulled out a vast painting of Rachel lying on a blazing sunlit beach, her slender body clad in a brief white bikini, her face young and lovely. He took it from the packing case, staring, thunderstruck.

'Oh!' Rachel's eyes lit up as she tried to take it from him.

'Who's it from?' he demanded tightly, checking the label.

'Tony!' she said, flushed with pleasure. 'He painted it when I was eighteen, on the beach at Chung Hom Kok, outside his parents' villa.'

Damian's mouth tightened. 'We can't accept it. It's unsuitable.'

'But why?' She was hurt. 'He probably thought you'd like it.'

'A painting of my wife half naked?' he said bitingly. 'I think not! Send it back immediately, or I'll take it back for you — and punch his impertinent face in while I'm at it!'

'Oh, I see!' She was shaking suddenly. 'We can accept the white silk sheets that your mistress sent, but not the painting Tony sent!'

'That's right!' he drawled, blue eyes glittering.

Fury made her reckless. 'Yes, that is right, isn't it? And who's surprised? Not me, not after meeting your family. No wonder you spend your time making women fight over you! It's been your lifelong experience of the opposite sex.'

He studied her for a second, eyes narrowed. 'Is that how you feel? That you're fighting over me with Domino?'

'No!' Appalled, she turned her face away, struggling for dignity.

There was a brief silence.

He came up behind her, drawled, 'Rachel, if you're jealous——'

'I'm not jealous, you bloody egoist!' she snapped, turning on him with blazing eyes. 'I just want my painting! Tony promised he'd give it to me on my wedding day, and I won't let you send it back!'

'No doubt he thought he'd be the one marrying you.' He smiled tightly.

'The answer to that is so obvious that I shan't bother to give it!'

There was a long silence. His face was rigid, his eyes glittering. 'I see,' he said thickly. 'And now he thinks he has the right to provoke me because of it? Well, we'll just see about that!' He turned on his heel, picked up the painting, and left the villa, slamming the door behind him.

Rachel ran after him, heart in her mouth. 'What are you doing?'

He thrust the painting in the Mercedes, got in, started the car and drove away without answering her, leaving scorch marks on the bleached stone courtyard. Rachel ran back into the villa, hands shaking as she dialled Tony's home number, then slammed the phone down before the call went through. If she rang Tony to warn him, Damian would guess that she had done so, and she didn't even want to consider his rage if he did. Ten minutes later, however, the phone rang. It was Tony.

'I knew I was pushing my luck,' he groaned over the phone. 'But I promised you that painting on your wedding day, and I had to send it.'

'What happened?' Rachel asked, heart beating raggedly.

'He roared down the drive a couple of minutes ago,' said Tony, 'slammed the car door, marched up to me, threw the painting on the beach, then punched me, told me to keep away from you, and roared away again.'

'Oh, no!' She was appalled. 'Tony, I'm so sorry! Are you badly hurt?'

'I'm not exactly feeling groovy! I think he dislocated my jaw.'

Appalled, she tried to soothe him down, and did not hear Damian enter the villa until he was right behind her.

'. . .he had no right to hit you like that!' Rachel was saying.

Damian snatched the phone from her hand, eyes like blue fire. 'Get the hell off this phone, Radcliffe!' he shouted thickly into the receiver. 'And don't ever call her again, or I'll come back and finish you off!' He slammed the phone down with a crash that must have hurt Tony's ears.

'How dare you speak to my friend like that?' Rachel shouted, beside herself with fury. 'You had no right——'

'Don't you ever listen to a word I say to you?' he bit out thickly. 'I told you to keep away from him and I meant it!'

'But that's unreasonable!' she flared. 'He's only a——'

'Rachel!' His eyes flared with blue violence. 'You're not to go near him again! Not ever—do you understand me?' He studied her white face for a second, then shouted, 'Do you understand me?'

Her mouth shook. 'Yes!'

'Good,' he said thickly, raking a hand through his hair, then turned and strode out of the villa, slamming the door behind him with a crash that reverberated through the house.

Next day, Rachel met Jenny at the airport. The night before the wedding, they went out to all their favourite haunts—1997, Rick's Café, the Go-Down—and ended up at two in the morning getting out of a taxi in Wan Chai, the neon blazing in the hot night, dark-eyed Chinese girls in brightly lit doorways, American sailors talking to them while people slept on the pavements and steaming noodles were served at three dollars a bowl at the poor-man's lean-to restaurant. They went into the House of Doom, the old English pub in the centre of all this, and took a corner booth.

As they drank coffee together, Rachel said, 'Jenny

. . .remember you talked about love with Damian that night he came to get me?'

Jenny nodded her red head. 'Yes?'

'Well,' Rachel chose her words carefully, 'I wondered why you talked about it. I mean — did he make a — a pass at you or —— ?'

'We talked about it,' said Jenny, 'because I told him frankly that I was in love with Jamie, and he looked at me as if I needed my head examined!' She laughed. 'I could see what he was thinking, so I started talking about love, how it means different things to different people, and that's when he said it.'

Rachel remembered the phrase word for word. 'That love was an erotic expression of the soul through the body?'

'Yes.' Jenny smiled. 'He said he'd read it somewhere a couple of years ago, and it had struck him so deeply that he couldn't shake it from his mind. He said he knew it sounded crazy, but ever since he'd read it he'd wanted to experience it, but had never met a woman who made him feel that way.'

Rachel looked at her and felt a spark of hope, knowing Damian did want, above and beyond all else, to make love to her. Could it be that he *did* feel something other than sexual desire for her?

Then she remembered his horror when he'd said, 'Don't tell me you're a virgin!' and her heart closed in on itself like a wounded animal. Damian considered her too inexperienced sexually to be able to fulfil that longing of his to express himself fully through the body.

Damian didn't love her and never would. He was just marrying her out of ambition — how many more times did she have to remind herself of that?

Next morning, all hell was let loose. Rachel stayed in her bedroom dressing, while she heard people

coming and going from the villa incessantly, her father
cheerful and everyone rushing around like mad trying
to get ready.

Nightingale came into her room with a beautiful
hairslide, cascades of white silk flowers falling from it.

'*M'goi, sai.*' Rachel thanked her in Cantonese.
'*Dochay.*'

'All Chinese brides wear one on their wedding day,'
Nightingale told her. 'You born in Hong Kong—you
get married in Hong Kong. You little bit Chinese, I
think. Pity about *guilo* skin and green eyes!'

Rachel decided she needed all the good luck she
could get. When she was fully dressed and made-up,
she called Jenny in to do her hair for her.

'Oh, Rachel. . .' Jenny stood back when she was
completely ready. 'You look so lovely!'

Turning to the mirror, she saw herself in the long
white silk dress, clinging to her slender body, curving
off the shoulders, accentuating her fine collarbones,
tight at the waist then flaring out with clouds of taffeta
below that made it seem as if she floated rather than
walked. Her black hair was piled in tiny ringlets, held
in place with a tiara from which fell a veil of embroid-
ered white lace. At the back of her hair, the white silk
flowers and pearls of the hairslide Nightingale had
given her gleamed softly beneath her veil.

'You're the most beautiful bride I've ever seen!'
Jenny said.

But Rachel did not feel like a bride. She stared at
her reflection and saw a woman whom the gods were
now punishing for her temerity in declaring she would
never be in the grip of uncontrollable emotion, and
here she was. . .here she was. . .

The thought of Damian made her heart wallop hard
against her breast. It can't be love. It mustn't be. He'd

destroy her if it was love, tear the heart from her and feast on it as the lion had that day in Auckland. Damian, her dark predator. . .

'Is the bride ready?' asked her father's cheery voice at the door.

A white limousine took them to the church. High on Victoria Peak, it overlooked the city through a faint mist, the sun breaking through to gleam on the sky-scrapers and the bay below.

'I'm so proud of you!' Charles squeezed her hand as they drove up the winding sunlit road to the peak. 'It's been such a burden, all these years. The company, the future, Jamie. . .now you've taken that burden from me, and I can relax at last, knowing it's all safe.' His eyes gleamed with tears. 'I knew as soon as I saw Damian that he was the son I'd never had, and now he is my son, in a way, isn't he?' He kissed her hand. 'Thank you, Rachel. You've made my life complete for the first time since your mother died.'

'I'm glad,' she said huskily, and her eyes sought his. 'Do you think there's any chance that you and Jamie will be reconciled now it's all over?'

He nodded with a dry smile. 'We're already trying to heal the long rift. I think we'll be actually be friends in a couple of years' time.'

The car drew up outside the church. Rachel stepped out into the sunlight, clouds of white silk and taffeta rustling as she moved with her father to the double doors. Jenny walked behind them, shimmering in green silk, her red hair adorned with tiny silk daisies.

Damian turned his dark head at the altar and her heart leapt raggedly. His blue eyes were dazzlingly powerful in his strong, tanned face. She felt weak with emotion at the sight of him, and the sound of his deep cool voice repeating the vows seemed to resonate in her heart.

'You may kiss the bride.'

He turned her to face him, lifted her lace veil, and the symbolic act sent a convulsive shudder of desire through her as a thought shot like fire into her mind. 'You're mine!' Her life had been spent running from possessive love, and now here she was, feeling it burn and twist inside her, pushing aside her conscious love of freedom to reveal the passionate woman beneath, dark and possessive, capable of fathomless emotion.

They were posing in hot, suffocating sunlight while people took photographs. Rachel's arms were around his neck, his hard mouth closing aginast hers, and she was lost in his kiss.

He raised his head, darkly flushed. 'You're mine!' he said thickly, and she held his gaze in a moment of wild hope that he could feel the same, then remembered the fight he had had to get her, and the prizes he was now about to collect. She turned from him in despair. His desire to possess her was rooted in the world of ambition, not the heart.

They were running to the car. Everyone clustered round them, calling greetings.

Suddenly, Rachel turned to throw her bouquet. In a flash, she saw Jenny's blaze of red hair, Jamie beside her, and she threw the bouquet above the heads of the others, straight at Jenny, who gasped and caught it. Jamie stared down at her, and Rachel turned away, sliding into the car.

'Rachel Flint,' Damian murmured, eyes narrowed as he sat back in the white limousine, watching her.

She shivered, looked down at the ring on her finger.

His hand touched the elegant curve of her bare shoulder. 'I'm going crazy. . .' he said thickly. 'Can't wait to make love to you. . . I wish we could go straight to bed instead of this bloody reception!'

Colour flooded her skin with hot response.

'The blushing bride,' he drawled softly, and leaned closer, his hot mouth against her neck. 'Looking forward to it too, my darling?'

'No!' she denied tightly, her pulses leaping like fire. 'I'm thinking about Tony! He should be here to see me married, but he didn't dare come after you punched his —'

'And I'll do it again, if you don't stop talking about him,' Damian bit out with sudden savagery, his hands hard on her bare shoulders.

'You can push him out of my life,' she said angrily. 'But you can't take him out of my head!'

'Yes, I damned well can, and we both know it,' he bit out. 'You may have memories of friendship with him, but I'm the man you want.' His voice roughened. 'And I'm the man you'll have tonight, when we reach Thailand!'

He had booked a beach house in Phuket, the island paradise on the coast of Thailand, for their honeymoon, and Rachel was both dreading it and clamouring for it.

He saw the excitement in her eyes. 'Oh, yes,' he said thickly. 'You're going to forget all about Radcliffe tonight!' And his hard mouth claimed hers in a burning kiss that sent her pulses racing, a muffled gasp of pleasure coming from her as her mouth opened hungrily beneath his.

The car stopped suddenly. The chauffeur gave a discreet cough. Damian raised his head, darkly flushed. 'Don't mention him again!' he said thickly, and a moment later they were stepping out into the sunlight at the Royal Hong Kong Cricket Club, the colonial sanctuary of Hong Kong Island with its Tudor pavilion, sweeping green lawns and the Union Jack flying against a halcyon blue sky.

The reception was held in the pavilion, trestle-tables covered in white linen and silver as the wedding breakfast was served and the speeches were made.

Night fell. The city began to light up, skyscrapers loomed beyond the walls like neon pillars against the dusk.

The dancing was held outside, in the open air behind the pavilion, a band playing hot jazz as Rachel and Damian led the dancing by the gleam of the swimming-pool, and the rhythm of their bodies as they moved blazed their desire for each other to the watching guests.

When the dance ended, he released her without a word and moved away to talk to his mother and sister, who had been crying passionately in the church as they watched Damian become Rachel's husband. As Damian spoke to them now, Katya and Lydia both glanced up to see Rachel standing alone on the dance area in her white bridal gown, watching Damian with intense passion in her green eyes. They both glared at her. She glared back, jealous and unable to hide her childish feelings. Suddenly, Lydia's mouth twisted in a wry smile, her eyes holding a spark of understanding. Rachel returned that smile, a glimpse of future pain and ecstasy, then turned to move among her own family and friends.

'Shouldn't you be getting ready to leave for Thailand?' her father asked her anxiously, glancing at his watch.

'Where's Jenny? She said she'd——' Rachel broke off, seeing the blaze of Jenny's red hair against Jamie's black evening suit. They were dancing very, very close.

Jamie's head was bent, his eyes closed, completely engulfed in Jenny. Rachel recognised the feeling.

'Damn it all!' Charles muttered beside her, and finished his frozen margarita. 'I'll go and peel her away from——'

'No.' Rachel put a hand on his arm.

He frowned, then his eyes darted back to Jenny. 'I say! You don't think they're——?'

'I wouldn't be surprised,' she said with a smile.

'Well!' said her father. 'That would be a blessing in disguise. If Jamie married and settled down we really could reconcile fast!'

Rachel went to a private room in the pavilion and changed into her going-away outfit, a green silk dress with a little matching bolero of thin silk to cope with the climates of both Hong Kong and Thailand.

The flight was quite short. After landing at Bangkok, they took a helicopter to the tiny Thai island of Phuket on the edge of the Indian Ocean. A mini-moke waited for them, and soon they were driving to the beach house through acres of Thai beachland and greenery. The moon was full, the dark waters of the ocean glittering with silver light, and the heat was stifling.

Insects buzzed in the hot night as they got out of the moke. The beach house was huge, well-lit, secluded from the road by lush plants and trees. A Thai girl was their maid, and she greeted them with a curtsy, took their cases up to their rooms and furnished them with cool drinks.

'We'll only require you for one hour a day. Make it midday; that'll be enough for us. You can go now.' Damian dismissed the maid, and she bowed silently, and left.

Rachel stood by the back porch doors, skin sheened

in the humid heat, heart beating raggedly as she faced
Damian, completely alone, on their wedding night.

He took her drink from her trembling hand. 'I think
it's time for bed,' he said softly. 'Don't you?'

She almost whimpered. . .

He led her up to the bedrooms, the floors and stairs
wooden, fans whirring overhead in the steamy heat,
mosquito netting over every door and window.

Damian opened the bedroom door, and as she
stumbled in he flicked on the light and the fan began
to whir softly above her head as she stood in the centre
of the room, the vast white double bed behind her, the
wooden floor warm beneath her feet.

Slowly, Damian locked the door behind them.

CHAPTER NINE

THE desire was pulsing in her veins, but beyond it lay emotion, such dark, intense emotion, and she knew the fight was over. The double bed glowed behind her. Damian stood in front of her. She had nowhere left to run.

I'm completely in love with him, she thought, and felt as though she had fallen, finally, at his feet.

She had fallen in love with him the minute she saw him, and she had known it, shied away from it, fought it, resisted, resisted, resisted. . .but love couldn't be resisted forever. It was a living force, unstoppable, growing like a plant through concrete if it had to, and, however desperately she had tried to trample her love down, it had finally reached the sun and was bathing in that brilliant golden warmth.

The stronger the conscious hate, she had read somewhere, the more powerful the unconscious love. And how she had hated him! With a passion, she realised now as every defence she had ever had fell away from her, and she felt the hatred swing round to reveal the love, deep and very passionate indeed.

As she admitted it, finally, it came for her, waves of love sweeping through her. The vulnerability she had long felt was the open heart she had tried to close as soon as she looked into those powerful eyes.

He took a step towards her, breathing hard. 'Rachel. . .!' he said huskily, reaching for her.

Rachel backed in terror. 'Don't come near me!'

Damian stopped dead, shock wiping his face clean of expression. 'What. . .?'

Her eyes were determined. She tried to get past him, running for the door, running for safety, running from the unspeakable truth—that she was ready to fall at his feet and admit her love.

He caught her wrist. 'What the hell are you doing?'

'Running from you!' she said bitterly. 'From this farce of a marriage!'

'You can't turn me down now!' he said hoarsely, jerking her hard against him, his eyes blazing. 'I don't believe it. . .! Rachel, for God's sake——'

She struggled in fierce silence, hitting out at him, her eyes wild with determination to escape.

'How dare you do this to me?' he bit out hoarsely, his hands shaking as he held her, his face darkly flushed with rage. 'How dare you?'

Rachel tried to bite his hand, desperate to escape.

'No, you don't!' he bit out thickly. 'After what you've put me through, I can't let you get away with this! My God, not if I have to kill you to keep you in this bedroom!'

'Let me go!' She fought bitterly, eyes wild.

'Do you have any idea of the hell I've been through? I had to practically bite my knuckles to keep my hands off you for the last three weeks, and I did it because of your innocence! I thought we had a deal. I thought we understood each other. I gave you time to adjust to the fact that I'd make love to you tonight and——'

'Love! Don't call it that!' Her voice shook. 'What a tragedy you are! What a travesty this marriage is! All you want from me is sex!'

'I told you I couldn't give you love!'

She flinched as though he had struck her. Then she hurled unthinkingly, 'Tony would have given me love!'

'You bitch. . .!' he said in a shaking voice. 'You bloody bitch!' And suddenly he dragged her struggling against him, and clamped her there while his hard mouth sought and found hers in a violent kiss, forcing her lips apart, his hand holding the back of her head like a vice while she kicked and hit and struggled.

The room was rippling with the sounds of their scuffle as they fought in bitter silence, knocking into wooden furniture, she trying to get away, he trying to get her to the bed until they fell against a nightstand and it crashed to the floor.

The lamp shattered at their feet.

They were next to the bed, still fighting.

'Radcliffe would have given you love, would he?' His voice was thickly clogged with some primitive emotion she assumed was rage.

'Yes! Love — not violence and rape!'

'It won't be rape! You want me!'

'No, I don't!' Her mouth was shaking. ' I want love, Damian. . .love!'

'Well, let's just see how well you do without it!' Damian bit out in a hoarse voice. 'Let's just see how necessary love is!'

'I won't let you take me!' she spat, kicking and struggling.

'If it's a fight you want,' he said thickly, catching her kicking legs and lifting her violently in his arms, 'you've got it!' He threw her on to the bed, his face red with rage. 'And I'll carry it on to the bitter end if that's what it takes!'

Rachel scrambled desperately for the other side of the bed.

'Come back!' He caught her ankle, lunging at her, took her by the shoulders and flung her on to her back, his breathing hoarse and his eyes blazing with fury. 'Stop fighting or I'll go completely crazy. . .!'

'Go to hell!' She jack-knifed up, tried to get away.

His hard body fell on hers, his hands pinning her wrists to the bed, his hard thigh parting hers and trapping her kicking legs. 'Don't push me much further, Rachel!' he bit out thickly as she fought. 'For God's sake. . .can't you see I'm already close to the edge?' He lowered his head, kissing her angrily, and she fought him, struggling beneath him as he kept her trapped, even though she offered such resistance to what he knew so deeply she had wanted from the beginning.

She clung on desperately for reprieve, but none came; he wouldn't stop, his mouth burning down over hers while he pinned her wrists to the bed, driven beyond his limits by her refusal, and she felt her breasts against his chest, her eyes open, seeing his face, hearing his hoarse breathing, the way he drew air into his lungs raggedly before lowering his head to kiss her again, his heart beating and his black hair tousled and his tie pulled loose in the scuffle. . .

A moan of hoarse emotion came from her lips.

There was a tense pause.

Damian lifted his head, breathing harshly, staring at her, and saw the fire in her green eyes.

He swallowed hard, then said shakingly, 'Kiss me. . .!'

Her mouth opened hungrily beneath his and she heard his hoarse intake of breath, his fingers relaxing fractionally on her wrists as his kiss grew deep and passionate, and she responded, kissing him back, her eyes closing and her head tilting back as her body arched softly against his.

'Yes. . .kiss me. . .!' he muttered thickly, and his

mouth moved over hers with anguished excitement. He
released her wrists. His long fingers moved over her
body, touching, caressing her hips, his mouth increasing the pressure, and she couldn't help herself; her
heart was going faster, faster. . .

Suddenly, she was clinging to him, her hands in his
dark hair, gasping with pent-up desire as his hands
swept up to her breasts. He stroked them, his fingers
tugged down her bodice, and when her breasts bounced
free she arched towards him passionately, and heard
him draw in his breath again, sharply, whispering, 'Oh,
God. . .!'

She moaned in pleasure as he touched her breasts.
Her hands were in his dark hair, her mouth kissing him
with all the love and desire she had suppressed for so
long. 'Damian. . .!' she whispered, saying his name as
though it was the most precious sound in the world,
gaining intense pleasure from it on her lips as though
she was really saying, I love you, I love you.
'Damian. . .!'

His eyes blazed with hunger. 'Yes. . .this is what I
want. . .this. . .' and they were both shaking as he
pushed the thin green silk dress from her body, throwing it to the floor, and came back to her at once, saying
thickly, 'Give me everything. . .make love with me. . .
make love!' and he kissed her deeply, making her
excitement deeper, hotter, until she was moving against
him, delirious, her body almost nude save for thin silk
briefs. He bent his head and his hot mouth closed
hungrily over her breast while she offered it to him
with one hand, her head thrown back, eyes closed,
surrendering to the hot, dark feel of his mouth sucking
at her nipple.

'Damian. . . Damian. . .!' Her voice sounded dark
and dangerously excited even to her own ears.

He tugged his silk tie off with strong hands, shrugging out of his jacket in a blur of darkly flushed
cheekbones and glittering, fevered eyes, then they were
together again.

Sweat dewed her lashes as she unbuttoned his white
shirt, pushing it from his broad shoulders, running her
hands over his flesh, pulling him closer, her mouth as
hungry as his. His heart was thudding hard against his
chest. His spine was sheened with heat and sweat. It
was what she had wanted to do since she met him —
touch him like this, feel his naked body against her.
Clothes were irrelevant. . .only flesh mattered to her
where Damian was concerned, because she did not just
want the hard, ambitious chairman of the board, but
the man of flesh and blood whom she loved more
powerfully than she could put into words, and only the
silent communication of their bodies allowed her to
express that love. . .

She was naked, completely naked, and she could
hear his harshly muttered words of desire; they excited
her beyond belief, her body twisting against his in
mindless fever, all flesh and blood and pulse.

One pulse beat higher and harder and faster than
any other, and as Damian touched it she gave a gasp
of shock, staring at him, and he arched above her, the
expression on his hard face making the blood roar in
her ears.

'Lie back. . .' he said thickly, his long fingers touching her boldly, and he stroked that throbbing pulse
with authority and experience, his mouth against hers,
his strong hand between her silken thighs. The pulse
beat faster, louder, harder, and she moaned as the
ecstasy spiralled, her breathing thick and rapid. 'Oh,
God!' Damian said hoarsely against her throat as he
stroked her. 'Yes. . . Rachel. . .!' And her moans grew

more frantic, faster, until she was panting harshly, sweat making her limbs slippery.

Inhibitions were crashing all around her mind and heart and body. Darkness was filling her, spiralling in harsh tension, his touch forcing her upwards towards ecstasy. As she heard him unzip his trousers, she whispered thickly, 'Yes. . . Yes. . .!' and felt him strip, the feel of his hair-roughened skin against hers driving her wild because now he was so real, so completely real, and so completely hers as they moved together naked, and she took the physical desire he expressed for her and pretended it was love, because it was the deepest display of emotion he had ever shown her.

She felt him naked between her thighs, felt the throb of his manhood against her slippery skin, and his long, expert fingers were still on the pulse that was taking her over, making her mad, driving her into wild darkness, and his voice said thickly, 'Rachel. . . Rachel. . .!' as though he was going mad, and he began to enter her, making her clutch at his body, gasping, becoming one with him, overwhelmed with emotion as her pulse grew faster, louder, harder. . .

With a hoarse cry she went into violent climax, her body possessed by the pulse that roared in her ears, her heart, her stomach, her thighs and made her limbs spasm and twist in ecstasy beneath him — no longer human, no longer conscious, no longer caring about anything except the dark flood of pleasure that rushed through her and shook her till she rattled and writhed to a hot, pulsing oblivion on his body.

Then the hard body overpowered her completely, thrusting into her, hands biting into her hips as she sprawled beneath him, her mouth slack and her eyes dazed, and as he looked down and saw the expression on her face he began to groan louder with pleasure,

whispering incoherent words in a ragged, dehumanised
voice, devastating her with the absolute possession he
took, sliding his hands under her rear, his face contort-
ing barbarically as he went into a violent climax in a
series of deep, fast thrusts and jerked against her with
a fierce cry, his body shaking as with the spontaneous
release of an electric current.

'Rachel. . . Rachel. . .!' He was breathless, his voice
sticky and incoherent as the breath was punched out of
him, his face delirious.

Rachel watched him and felt the dam burst, smashing
back the last barriers to her soul, and flooding her with
a rush of overwhelming emotion.

His head dropped on to her breast. He lay there,
shuddering, dragging air into his lungs, heart slamming,
blood pulsing round his body.

Love was pouring through her and she could not
stop it, lying beneath him, helpless to prevent the tears
which sprung to her eyes and rolled over her cheeks.
Her arms went round his shoulders, she buried her hot,
wet face in his throat, kissing the pulse that beat so
rapidly there, and she felt so moved, so deeply in love,
that a hoarse sob escaped her lips and a second later
she was dragging air into her lungs in a shaky breath
filled with emotion. In those moments, those final
moments as he took her and reached ecstasy, she had
been able to believe he loved her, felt something for
her; and, though she knew he did not, she was moved,
wanted to retain those precious moments which he had
just given her when he had finally stripped the mask
away and let her see how human he was as he merged
with her and lost himself inside her.

Damian lifted his dark head to stare at her. He saw
the tears.

'What is it?' his voice asked huskily. 'Did I hurt you?

Darling, I did everything I could to make it pleasurable, not painful. . .'

He thought her pain was physical, of course, and his voice was only rendered husky by the sexual experience he had just had. He was still the hard, ambitious man who had married her for her father's company, not for love. Her eyes stung with fresh tears. I can never tell him I'm in love with him, she thought, and the sense of loss was appalling.

'Rachel. . .?' He was staring at her, frowning.

She had to reply. Had to come up with something convincing. 'I gave my innocence to your ambition instead of to a man I loved!' she heard her husky voice say. 'That's enough to make any woman cry.'

He stared at her, the colour draining from his face.

Rachel couldn't look at him. The tears were falling hotly down her cheeks, and she buried her face in his hot neck, a hoarse sob coming unbidden from the back of her throat.

'Oh, for God's sake!' he said thickly, then put a hand to her damp head, clutching her to him. 'Don't cry. . . Rachel, don't. . .!' He breathed unevenly as she sobbed against his throat. 'Sssh!'

'Damian,' she whispered hoarsely, 'I. . . I'd like to be alone now. Would you mind? There must be more bedrooms in this house, surely?'

There was a tense silence. His fingers were suddenly rigid against her scalp and she heard his heart drumming with rage.

'Yes, I would mind!' he bit out thickly.

Her eyes darted to his. 'But you've got what you wanted. Surely that's enough for one night!'

'No, it's not enough,' he said through his teeth. 'I want to make love to you again!'

'Again?' Her pulses quickened as she stared.

'Yes, again! Don't look so surprised! You must be able to feel me stirring inside you!' His breathing quickened. 'I only have to look at you to want you. . . don't you have any idea what you do to me?'

Her face ran with colour. She was excited despite herself, her eyes darkening, staring through black lashes, her mouth parting with unconscious invitation as she moistened her lips and lowered her hot gaze to his chest.

'Oh, God. . .!' Damian said unsteadily, and bent his head to kiss her mouth with slow, sensual desire, and that was how they made love, their bodies moving as slowly but surely towards that ecstasy as that initial kiss did, until Rachel, this time, was breathless and incoherent, delirious with pleasure as she reached climax through his strokes and expertise and unbelievably exciting lovemaking.

They made love a third time before falling into an exhaustion that was beyond pleasure, their naked bodies sprawled together, arms and legs tangled, and when they woke up late the next day Damian made love to her again until her eyes closed and she shuddered in hot delirium against him. Then they got up and ate hungrily on the hot porch, then sunbathed in the sweltering heat, lying in each other's arms on the white beach, talking softly as the sea rippled beyond them.

They swam then, and Damian made love to her in the hot sea, stripping her as they floated together, wrapping their bodies around each other in unreasoning desire, kissing saltily as their hoarse cries filled the air and they nearly sank like stones as Damian went rigid with pleasure, his fingers biting into her nude body in the warm water.

'No more talk of love?' Damian asked during a lull

in their lovemaking on the second day. 'We don't need it, do we?' He kissed the damp pulse at her throat as she gasped for breath, exhausted with pleasure. 'Not us, Rachel. . .we have this. . .'

'What do we have?' she asked raggedly, eyes intent on him. 'Put a name to it, Damian, before I go mad. . .'

He hesitated, then drawled softly, 'We're lovers, my darling. It's what we were born to do together, and it's heady stuff, you must admit. . .'

'Headier even than love?' she whispered, kissing his bare chest.

'Headier by far. . .' he said huskily. 'This insatiable need, this thirst, this ungoverned passion. . .'

'Yes,' she said softly, a hand at her eyes to shade the glare of the sun as they lay naked and wrapped together on the hot, deserted beach. 'Ungoverned passion. . .'

It at least described some kind of emotional response from Damian, and that was what she needed more than anything else. Without it, she could not have given herself to him so completely. When he made love to her, she was able to believe he felt something—something—for her.

Their days began to form a hot, sensual routine. They would waken late, naked in each other's arms, sprawled together, limbs tangled from their fierce lovemaking the night before. Then Damian would start to caress her, his hands wringing that torturous response from her, and they would make love again until they sprawled together in exhaustion. Hunger then tended to strike, forcing them out of that sinful bed, and down to the sunlit kitchen to make breakfast of fruit and coffee and rolls.

In the afternoons they sunbathed and swam. Rachel's skin turned dusky gold. She took to living in her swimsuit, a colourful sarong tied at her hips, long black hair streaming loose and silken down her slender back, and Damian would watch her with intent eyes as she moved around the house, his eyes eating her up as she grew more and more sensual, her inhibitions almost completely erased by his lovemaking.

'I love it when you do that. . .' she whispered to him one day as they made love, and he laughed softly, looking down at her, such warmth in his face that her heart stopped and her smile faded.

Damian's smile faded too. 'What is it?' he asked at once. 'What are you thinking?'

She hesitated, hope so fragile that she was afraid to risk rejection. 'I. . . I just thought. . .when you smiled at me just then that. . .'

'What? Tell me!' he commanded.

'Well, that. . .' Her face was burning, then she said in a rush, 'That this desire we share could grow, maybe into a deep affection. I mean, you looked at me with . . .with something like love just then——'

'I love your body and making love with you,' he said deeply, his own body tense against hers as he spoke. 'Nothing else!'

It was her own fault for asking, and she paid the price, pain tearing at her heart as Damian bent his head and continued making love to her until she reached a bitter-sweet ecstasy in his arms, and after that she never mentioned love again. She couldn't take the risk any more. The rejections he kept kicking into her heart were leaving terrible scars. All she had was his husky voice as he made love to her, his body against hers, and the chance to pretend to herself that he might love her as he expressed emotion through lovemaking day after day, night after night. . .

As the hot sun set beyond the glittering turquoise

waters of the Indian Ocean, they would move inside to
escape the mosquitoes and other creatures of the night.

They ate less and less, never venturing outside the
villa, the physical aspect of their relationship consum-
ing them both as Damian began to take her beyond her
new-found sensuality, smashing barriers as he went,
teaching her everything about her body and his until
she thrilled to the power of knowing how to touch and
kiss him to make him breathless with ecstasy, whispering incoherent, urgent words of encouragement to her
until they both fell into their usual sleep of pleasurable
exhaustion, completely united by the passion that raged
just as highly between them now as it ever had from
the very beginning. And, strangely, the pain receded,
replaced by the absolute intimacy and physical trust
between them as the honeymoon took them deeper
and deeper into the waters of sexual love.

When the last day came, Rachel felt the atmosphere
between them change.

They awoke in each other's arms as usual, but when
Damian made love to her there was an edge to it, an
urgency that frazzled her, made her pleasure sharply
intense, pain mingling with her cries as he took her
with him into the dark, hot void they shared.

When his breathing returned to a steady pace, he
said coolly, 'We'd better pack after breakfast.'

'Yes. . .'

They did not look at each other as they spoke, and
when Damian moved away from her he avoided her
eyes.

The pain began, slowly at first, then, as though the
knife-blade had been turned back to her heart by his
subtle withdrawal from her, it began to enter her heart;
and then it began to revolve.

At three o'clock that afternoon, the intimacy

between them had almost completely disintegrated. When she went into the bedroom to get her suitcase, she found Damian Flint, chairman of the board, standing at the window in a grey Savile Row suit, his face hard and remote, gold watch-chain glittering across his formal waistcoat.

He turned from the window, and she saw the mask was back in place. 'We should go. Our helicopter is waiting.'

'Of course,' she said expressionlessly, but inside she was devastated by the loss of her sensual lover. He had gone forever, to be replaced by the man she had really married, the ambitious and powerful Damian Flint.

For the first time in her life, she was hurt by the sight of Hong Kong, that beautiful neon city, glittering like a great gaudy Ferris wheel on the edge of China and signifying the absolute end of her dream with Damian, the end of an enclosed world with no past or future, only the sensual present, leading them further and further into pleasure without limit or consequence.

Reality had been suspended in that secluded Thai beach house, in that paradise of Phuket. The trust that had made their intimacy possible did not exist outside it. Just the sight of Hong Kong's skyscrapers and sophisticated city lights made the very last traces of that trust vanish into thin air.

As they disembarked from the jet, they were strangers.

'Where the hell is Bennet?' Damian said impatiently as he strode away from Passport Control.

'Perhaps he's waiting outside.' Rachel's voice was hurt and remote.

His mouth tightened. He flashed an angry look around the airport.

'Sir!' Bennet was hurrying towards them in his smart grey uniform.

'Take the cases!' said Damian bitingly, his hand gripping Rachel's arm and marching her out through the sliding doors to the limousine.

They drove through the brightly lit city streets of Tsimshatsui, and it was like hurtling back to earth through the atmosphere; Rachel felt she was being shaken till her teeth rattled as the car sped up through the cross-harbour tunnel into Causeway Bay, past the bobbing sampans and the escort clubs, speeding towards Central District along the harbour road, traffic everywhere, horns blasting in her ears. . .

Until she let go, finally, of the memory of that sensual paradise they had shared in Phuket and bowed, defeated, before the brutal ambition of Hong Kong.

The city seemed to glitter in hard, implacable triumph.

Ambition and power could not be swayed by love or foolish dreams, and the message was not lost on Rachel as she faced the reality of her marriage now that the honeymoon — how clichés suddenly made sense! — was over.

They were alone in his villa.

Rachel faced him across that beautiful living-room and knew her sensual lover had gone forever. This was the real Damian Flint, and the mask of ruthless ambition he wore was his true self. In that moment, she almost broke down and told him she loved him desperately, for she could see, finally, that all her pretences in Thailand of his capacity for emotion had been just that: pretences. Damian felt nothing for her. He never would. What difference could it possibly make if she told him she loved or hated him? He would

simply look at her with that hard mask and feel
nothing.

'Come to bed!' he said abruptly into the silence.

She turned away, pain in her heart. 'I'm rather tired
tonight. . .'

'Tired!' His face hardened. He reached for her.

'No!' Rachel said, backing. 'It was different in
Thailand! We were on honeymoon, I could do it
without loving or being loved, but not here. . .not in
Hong Kong. . . I can't, Damian; please don't make
me!'

'Why?' he bit out thickly. 'Because Radcliffe's only
ten minutes away from you?'

Rachel looked at him carefully. 'I didn't say that. . .'

His eyes flared with rage. 'No, you didn't have to,
you little bitch; I could see it from the minute we
arrived! Now come to bed!' And he strode to her,
grabbing her wrist and tugging her upstairs.

He made love to her angrily. 'I'll force that little
bastard out of your head if it's the last thing I do!' he
bit out, hatred on his face as he took her, made love
like the enemy he was.

They fell asleep in each other's arms, and Rachel
cried bitter tears in silence against his chest, mourning
her lost lover. . .

Next morning, she woke to find him already up and
dressed, standing in front of the full-length mahogany
mirror in his stark masculine bedroom, tying a dark
red silk tie at his throat, his back to her, the silk gleam
of his waistcoat yet another symbol of his obsession
with power and wealth.

'Where are you going?' Rachel asked huskily from
the bed.

He tensed, eyes shooting to hers in the mirror. Then
he said flatly, 'To work. Where do you think?'

She swallowed. 'But you're not expected back until tomorrow. I remember you saying that you'd take the day off after we got back from Thailand. . .'

'And what would I do with it?' he drawled unpleasantly. 'Sit around talking to you? I had enough of that on our honeymoon!'

Her face tightened with bitter pain. She was white.

'I'm bored.' Damian turned, hands thrust in grey trouser pockets. 'I want to get back to the office.'

'You mean you want to get away from me!' she burst out, shaking suddenly, her eyes blazing.

He gave a harsh laugh, then turned, picked up his jacket with one strong hand from the back of a chair and opened the bedroom door. 'I'll be gone until late tonight. Spend the day as you wish—but don't go within a mile of Radcliffe or I'll break every bone in his body. Got it?'

He went out without another word, and she heard him going down the stairs. She sat in bed, white-faced, and listened to the flare of the Mercedes limousine as the chauffeur drove Damian into Central.

Tears stung her eyes. She wept into her hands, then felt utterly defeated, lying sprawled across the bed weeping herself into exhaustion until she lay still, staring at nothing, no tears left.

Footsteps on the landing made her tense. There was a knock at the door, then it opened. 'Oh!' A Filipino woman of about thirty stared at her. 'So sorry, Mrs Flint! I do this room later!'

The door closed. Rachel sat up. I can't stay here crying with the amah wandering around, she realised, and went into the luxurious master bathroom to bathe and change.

Later, she went out shopping, taking a taxi to Jardine's Bazaar down in Causewsay Bay. The huddle

of noisy stalls in the back streets were a clamour of life
and colour, selling diamanté, silk ribbons, radios,
clothes, dead fish sliced up on cold slabs, snakes split
down the middle, innards steaming on the bloodied
stone floors, live birds in cages, killed with a hammer
then plucked and sold, and thousand-year-old eggs
streaked black and white with gaudy orange centres.

Rachel bought absurd things, then went back to the
villa, and unpacked all her useless purchases, aware
that she had bought a ridiculous diamanté choker to
cheer herself up, and now felt a fool.

Holding the choker in her hand, she heard the
amah's flip-flops coming downstairs. Rachel looked
around the living-room for a hiding place for her
choker. She ran to the polished mahogany bureau,
opened the lid and threw the choker on to a pile of
papers.

Above the glitter of the diamonds, she saw the words
'FLINT IVESTMENTS LTD.'

Rachel froze, staring at that black printed insignia.

The amah flip-flopped in. 'Hello, Mrs Flint!' she
called cheerfully. 'You go shopping?'

'Yes. . .' Rachel was still staring at the paper.

'FLINT INVESTMENTS LTD. WILLOW AND WALL. NEW
YORK, NEW YORK.'

Her heart was beating very, very hard.

She looked down at the bold black signature and the
printed words below it: 'Damian Flint, Chairman.'

'I make coffee,' said the amah. 'You want some?'

Rachel was beyond speech, staring at the paper in
the bureau.

The telephone shrilled between them.

'No, thank you,' Rachel said in a voice rendered
blank with shock, and reached out a hand to the
telephone beside the bureau. 'Hello. . .?'

The line clicked, long distance, then crackled.

'Hi!' an American voice drawled. 'Am I speaking to the radiant bride?'

Rachel struggled to deal with this disembodied voice. 'I'm Mrs Flint. I'm afraid my husband isn't here. Who shall I tell him called?'

'Jack Bernstein in New York,' he drawled. 'Is he in the Swift office today? This is a matter of some urgency, Mrs Flint, and I——'

'Is it to do with his New York investment house?' Rachel heard her voice say suddenly.

'Well, that's right, Mrs Flint. Something's come up and——'

'Can I take a message?' she said on a sudden flare of hope. 'I might be able to see him for lunch in half an hour.'

There was a pause. 'I guess there wouldn't be any harm in it. . .tell him Bachman Hart are stalling on the deal. Bachman says he'll only talk to Damian.'

Rachel's heart thudded but she needed irrefutable proof. 'Bachman will only talk to the chairman of the board himself? My husband?'

Jack Bernstein laughed. 'I guess that's the message in a nutshell!'

Minutes later, Rachel was running out on to the road, hailing a taxi and driving off into Central.

Damian was already chairman of his own investment house in New York! On Wall Street! He was already rich, powerful, successful beyond anything Swift could have given him, and that meant only one thing—he had not married her to become chairman of a vast investment house, because he was already chairman of his own!

That could mean only one thing: he loved her.

Tears of joy made her mouth shake, but she forced

them back, refusing to risk such annihilation if she was
wrong, if he didn't love her. She would just confront
him with the fact that she knew about Flint Investments
of New York, and see what he said.

The taxi pulled up outside Swift on Des Voeux.

Rachel was hunting in her bag for a twenty-dollar
bill.

Suddenly, the white Mercedes pulled up in front of
the taxi, the doors of Swift swung back, and Damian
walked across the hot pavement with Domino Mei-
Ling in his arms.

CHAPTER TEN

FOR a long time, Rachel just sat there, white with pain. The smoked-glass doors of Swift were closed and the Mercedes had long ago pulled into the traffic, but she just kept seeing it in her mind, Damian striding along with his arm around the beautiful Domino.

'Thirty-five dollar, miss.'

Rachel blinked, staring at the Chinese taxi driver. Then she remembered she hadn't paid him. That was good; it gave her something to think about other than the pain lacerating her heart. She couldn't go into the building. Not now. Not with Domino in there. She tried to think what she should do. Not go back to the villa — she couldn't be alone. Not to her father's villa — he'd expect her to be a radiant bride just back from her honeymoon. There was only one place she could go to.

'Chung Hom Kok, *m'goi*,' she said tightly to the driver, and leant back against the blue leather seats as they pulled away.

Tony was on the beach outside his family's villa, listening to music and sunbathing. The taxi drove down the winding white drive and Tony got up, coming towards her with a frown.

'Is something wrong? I thought you only just got back from you homeymoon. . .'

'I just needed to see you!' she said with a brittle smile, walking past him on to the hot beach, feeling the tears burn her eyes.

163

Tony was with her, taking her shoulders. 'Are you all right? You look as though you've been cry——'

'I'm fine!' she said thickly, then smiled again. 'Can I sit with you and sunbathe for a while? Damian's gone to work and I'm bored all alone at the villa with nothing to do.'

He studied her for a moment, then said slowly, 'Of course. I'm always happy to see you, you know that. Want something to drink? Fruit punch? Pimm's?'

'Pimm's. . .' she said huskily, grateful he did not ask any painful questions, questions she could not have answered.

Tony pootled off into the villa. Rachel sat there alone, staring blankly at the turquoise sea as it rippled softly on white sand. The pain she felt went beyond jealousy this time. It was touching despair, so deep that she could not cope.

Tony came back and handed her a tall glass of iced Pimm's filled with fruit, then flopped on to the sun-lounger beside her, smiling in his uncomplicated way.

'He asked me once,' she said huskily, 'if I was predator or prey.'

Tony frowned. 'If you were what. . .?'

'Predator or prey,' she whispered, and buried her face in her hands.

'Darling!' Tony sat up, put his arms around her, holding her close. 'Don't cry. . .please!'

The sound of a car engine broke the silence as they embraced, and Rachel looked up, frowning blankly as a white Mercedes screeched down the white drive and jerked to a halt.

'Uh-oh!' Tony said slowly, still holding Rachel.

She stared at the car. 'Damian. . .!'

He got out, slammed the door, his face dark with rage. 'Get your hands off my wife!'

'Now just a minute, let me expl——' Tony began.

'I said get your hands off her!' Damian was striding over to them.

Rachel stumbled to her feet. 'I was crying! He comforted——'

'How touching! Forgive me if I don't ask how you feel, but I'm just going to break every bone in your boyfriend's body!' Damian's voice rose in fury as he strode to them, reached them and pushed Tony away from Rachel with a violence that made her cry out in horror as Tony stumbled backwards.

'No! Don't hit him!' She leapt forward.

Damian lunged after Tony, his face dark with rage as he bit out thickly, 'You're like a bloody wasp, stinging at me — driving up in your red sports car, honking your horn, taking her dancing all over town, kissing her behind my back, sending me a painting of her half naked for my wedding present!' He caught him by the shirt. 'And now you ring her up on the day we get back from our honeymoon and get her to come down and tell you all about it! I could take you apart limb from limb and God himself would call it justice!'

'He didn't ring me!' Rachel screamed.

'Liar!' Damian bit out. 'My amah told me you left in a hurry after a phone call from a man!'

'But it wasn't Tony who rang me! It was Jack Bernstein!'

There was a silence. Damian stared at her. Tony was cowering away, shaking as Damian held him by the lapels of his shirt.

'It was Jack Bernstein!' Rachel said again, shaking with fury. 'And I came up to Swift to deliver his message personally! I thought we might have lunch! But you already had a lunch date, didn't you?' Jealousy flared in her eyes as she spat: 'I saw you take Domino

Mei-Ling back into the offices! You had your arm
around her! So don't come here accusing me of——'

'What the hell are you talking about?' Damian
released Tony with a violent shove, strode to Rachel,
caught her by the shoulders, his face fierce. 'What did
Jack tell you? Did he say that I was——?' He broke off
suddenly, his face rigid, then swore violently, pushing
her from him, turning his back, raking a hand through
his dark hair.

There was a silence. The turquoise sea lapped softly
at the hot white sands.

Tony shuffled uncertainly. 'Perhaps you dudes
should be alone to talk this——'

'Shut the hell up, Radcliffe!' Damian snarled, whirling on him. 'I'm going to get the truth out of my wife,
and if I find out there's anything going on between you
I'll be back here to use you as a punchbag! And as for
your friends, please feel free to invite them along! I've
long wanted to knock the groovesome dudes over like
a pack of skittles!' His eyes blazed with menace. 'Got
it?'

Tony kicked at the sand, his face set. 'Yes, I've got
it!'

Damian dragged Rachel to the Mercedes, thrust her
in the front sea, got in beside her, started the engine
with a roar and crunched the gears as he did an angry
U-turn then roared up the drive with a screech of tyres.

'You've got a nerve!' Rachel said bitterly as they
shot on to the main road. 'Charging down here like a
maniac, trying to hit——'

'You're lucky I didn't beat him to death!' he bit out,
the car screeching round the mountain road in hot
sunlight. 'It's what I've wanted to do for a long time,
so long that I can't remember a time when the name
Tony Radcliffe didn't send me into a violent rage!' He

flung her a furious look. 'So don't tell me I've got a nerve! I deserve the Nobel Peace Prize for not having torn him to pieces already!'

He careened the car into the courtyard of his villa. It leapt in the air as it shot over the ramp, making Rachel gasp as she watched him slam the brakes on, flinging her forward to make the seatbelt dig into her.

'My God, you really are a dangerous—' she began.

'That's right,' he said thickly. 'And I'll get more dangerous as this marriage wears on unless you stay away from him!' He got out of the car, slammed the door, strode round and hauled her out, dragging her into the villa behind him.

He dragged her into the living-room and flung her across it to skid to a halt.

Damian slammed the door, breathing hard. 'All right! Let's get the truth!' He strode to her. 'You say Bernstein called! Is that the beginning of your convoluted little story?'

'It's not convoluted!' she spat. 'You're convoluted! You! With your double-standards and preoccupation with sex and—'

'Just stick to the story' he bit out. 'Bernstein rang! What did he say? Anything in particular? Or did he just leave a message to let me know he'd called?'

Rachel breathed hard, hating him. 'There's no point in trying to cover your tracks, Damian! Even if Jack Bernstein hadn't let the cat out of the bag I would have known!'

'And what do you know?' he bit out thickly.

'That you're already chairman of an international investment bank!' she said bitterly. 'That you didn't need to marry me to fulfil your ambitions! They were already fulfilled long before you ever met me!'

He gave a harsh laugh. 'Good detective work!'

'I saw a letter in your bureau,' she said tightly. 'It had the Flint Investments insignia at the top and your signature at the bottom with chairman printed under it.'

'And when did you find that?' he drawled thickly. 'How long have you known?'

'I found it just before Jack Bernstein rang. And, before you ask, I wasn't snooping around!' Her eyes flared. 'I was looking for a hiding place for some stupid necklace I'd bought, and the bureau was the nearest thing to hand!'

He looked away, face darkly flushed. 'Go on with your story. What happened after the call from Jack?'

'I took a taxi to Swift offices. I was just about to pay the driver when your car pulled up in front of me and you got out with Domino.'

'Why did you get a taxi?' he asked, watching her intently, his body very still. 'I mean — why come personally? Why not just pick up the phone and call me?'

She gave a defensive shrug. 'I had nothing better to do!'

His smile was hard. 'It wasn't because you wanted to see me, then?'

Rachel's heart beat fast with panic. 'Look, what is all this? What has this to do with —— ?'

'You'd just found out I was chairman of an even bigger company than Swift!' he bit out. 'What went through your mind as you drove to the office to see me?'

'I can't remember!'

He strode to her, eyes blazing, and shouted, 'Why did you specifically come to see me the minute you found out I had my own investment bank?'

She could barely breathe, her heart pounding so hard that she had to shout shakily, 'Because I knew it meant you couldn't have married me for my father's company, and I wanted to find out why you'd lied about it.' She felt vulnerable, afraid. 'I suppose I'd still like to know why. . .'

He gave a tight smile, drawled, 'I don't want to answer that until we've got to the end of your story.'

'That should give you time to think of a plausible excuse!' she said bitterly.

'Let's hope so!' he mocked. 'Go on with your story.'

Jealousy flared in her green eyes. 'I got to the office and saw you with Domino!'

'And how did you feel about that?' he asked thickly. 'I mean—you said you went straight to Radcliffe's because of it. It must have had one hell of an impact on you!'

'God, you're detestable!' she said, shaking.

His mouth tightened. 'Did you think it gave you *carte blanche* to see him? I imagine you've long wanted to share a physical relationship with Radcliffe. Now would seem the ideal opportunity to——'

'No, I didn't think that!' she said bitterly. 'I'm not sex-obsessed like you are!'

'You were in Thailand!' he drawled unpleasantly.

Hot colour flooded her face. 'Why, you——'

'Just stick to the story! How did you feel when you saw me with my beautiful Oriental mistress?'

Her breath caught, something inside her exploded, and she flew at him, hitting him blindly.

He caught her wrists, pinned them to her sides, eyes blazing.

'Does it make you feel good to humiliate me?' Rachel cried hoarsely, shaking. 'You've been asking me for weeks if I'm jealous! What is it—some sort of sick game?'

'*Are* you jealous?' he whispered thickly, his heart

beating hard as he crushed her to his chest. 'Tell me
. . .tell me!'

'Yes!' she shouted. 'Yes, yes, I'm jealous! I'm so
jealous I can't even think straight when——'

'Oh, Rachel!' he bit out thickly, burying his face in
her hair. 'She's not my mistress! She never has been!'

Rachel carried on fighting, hoarse gasps coming from
her throat.

'I made it all up!' he said against her neck. 'She's not
my mistress! She's not. . .'

'What?' Her struggles ceased, her head snapping
back, staring in shock, her heart pounding harder and
harder. 'What. . .?'

'She's not my mistress!' he said under his breath. 'I
let you think she was because I wanted to make you
jealous. That's all. That's all there's ever been to it.
Domino Mei-Ling is my secretary, nothing more. She
had a month off work while you filled in, then started
again as my secretary last week.' He lifted his dark
head. 'When you saw me with her today, I had my arm
around her because she was crying. Her mother's very
ill. I picked her up from the hospital on my way back
from a meeting on Kowloon-side. That's all there was
to it.'

Rachel stared at him in shock, then said hoarsely, 'I
don't believe you. You're just saying that to keep the
marriage together! You're afraid I'll go to my father
and tell him——' She broke off, staring.

There was a brief silence.

Damian's black lashes flickeed. He released her
suddenly, turning to walk to the french windows, his
hands thrust in grey trouser pockets, and stood there
in that open doorway, framed by the heat and dust and
the glittering ocean beyond the balcony.

'But. . .if you don't need Swift Investments. . .' she

could barely breathe '. . .and if Domino Mei-Ling is not your mistress. . .'

There was another long silence. Rachel's mind was jammed with frantic thoughts. But none of them made sense. He didn't need the company. Domino wasn't his mistress.

'I don't understand. . .' she whispered thickly. 'Why did you marry me if you —— ?'

'I left New York two years ago,' Damian cut in thickly, looking out to sea, his back to her. 'Moved to Hong Kong. It wasn't planned. I just got off the plane here and fell in love with the place, so I stayed. I guess I needed to fall in love with something. Hell, I'd spent most of my life dedicating myself to my work.'

Rachel moved slowly towards him, her eyes intent on his dark, handsome profile.

He sensed her presence, but didn't look at her. 'When I got here,' he said expressionlessly, 'I realised I needed to be in love with more than just a city. But I had this lifelong problem, you see.' He gave a cool laugh, drawled, 'I guess you could call it the madonna-whore complex.'

Rachel stood at his side, staring at him, her breath held.

'I knew two sorts of women,' he said thickly, not looking at her, 'the women I loved but didn't want to go to bed with. And then the women I did want to go to bed with, but couldn't conduct a conversation with.'

She waited, her heart beating so fast she was surprised she was still standing.

'I figured,' Damian said with a hard smile, 'that there must be a woman somewhere in the world who could be both. A woman I could love as well as want to go to bed with. I looked and looked, read a lot of books on

the subject, had a lot of late-night conversations with
people. . .'

'Like Jenny?' she whispered, and clutched the door-
jamb behind her, leaning against it for support, directly
parallel to him.

'Yes, I told her my theory,' he said under his breath.
'That when the two combine it's love. I mean—it has
to be, doesn't it? Much as I like to believe a man can
have sex with any woman and enjoy it, it just doesn't
stand the test.' He shot her cool glance through his
black lashes, and murmured, 'You'd have to be a man
to know what I meant.'

Rachel nodded jerkily.

'And when you love a woman,' he said under his
breath, 'it doesn't necessarily follow that you want to
express that physically. Catch 22. How do you find a
woman with both? It would be a chemical explosion—
but from the emotions; not the body.'

Rachel stared at him and wondered how much longer
she could hold her breath without dying. He was going
to say it. . .he had to be leading up to 'I love you'. . .
and she felt she was clinging on by her fingernails to
the last trace of hope, her hands clutching the door-
jamb behind her to stop herself sliding down and
begging him to say it.

'So I stayed in Hong Kong, flew back and forth to
New York, worked at Swift to keep myself busy, and
fended off a lot of very annoying letters from my
mother and sister, both incessantly wondering when I
was going to come to Kenya and put myself through
their combined emotional wringer.'

Rachel stared at his profile. She was trembling from
head to foot.

'Meanwhile, of course,' he said with a sardonic smile,
'I had the occasional woman.'

Her face tightened with jealousy, terrible jealousy; she didn't know how she'd bear it if he started to talk about other women. . .

'I slept with a few.'

Her fingers were biting into the metal.

'But it didn't work out. Nothing worked out. I hated making love to women I didn't even like. And I couldn't bear to be with women I did like because it reminded me forcibly that they didn't turn me on.'

She exhaled a shaking breath.

'So about a year ago I knocked the whole thing on the head. I didn't want any woman unless it was her. The one I was looking for. The one who had both.'

Please say it, she thought; please. . .please. . .

'Then one night,' he said thickly, 'about six weeks ago, I was in London when a girl in a red dress walked into the room and——'

Rachel flew into his arms, saying shakingly, 'Damian, I love you! I love you. . . I love you. . .!'

He buried his dark head in her throat, breathing hard. 'Oh, thank God. . .!' He was holding her very close, but his body was almost weak with relief against her. 'Rachel. . .!'

Rachel kissed him, her hands on his broad shoulders. 'Say it!' she begged, all pride gone. 'Please. . .please, say it!'

'I love you!' he said shakingly, and bent his dark head to kiss her, desire flaring between them, relief mingling sweetly with it, their mouths clinging and their arms round each other obsessively, twining together like bindweeds on that hot terrace with the scarlet bougainvillaea trailing down the dusty cliffs and the sea glittering turquoise beyond.

When Damian raised his head, he was darkly flushed, dragging air into his lungs. He held her against him, and she heard his heart beating hard against his powerful chest.

'I thought you loved Radcliffe,' he said thickly. 'I thought you loved him and fancied me. I've been through hell, Rachel, believing you had the same problem as me, and I was the man you wanted to go to bed with but couldn't stand personally.'

'Nothing could be further from the truth!' she whispered against his chest. 'Darling, I've been in love with you for so long, fighting it, hiding it from you. . . I kept saying all those things about Tony because I was desperate to stop you realising how I felt.'

'The more you talked about him with love, the more devastated I felt,' he said deeply. 'I was jealous of Radcliffe from the start because he was with you the night we met. You were so completely his, calling him darling, kissing him goodbye, telling me you were childhood sweethearts. . .'

She stared into his face. 'I was being flippant!' she said shakily. 'You seemed so dismissive, made me feel insignificant.'

He sighed deeply, and said with lifted brows, 'Dismissive! You have no idea. . . I was absolutely knocked breathless by you, Rachel. When you went to pack that first night, I hung around in the hall trying to figure out my best move. Should I ask you out straight away? Or wait till we got back to Hong Kong? And then the door opened and you walked out saying——'

'That I didn't find you remotely attractive!' she groaned, laughing and burying her face on his chest. 'Oh, no. . .!'

'Oh, yes!' he drawled, laughing too, but she could still hear the tension in his voice and she knew she had to tell him everything.

'I only said it because I was jealous of Jenny and

didn't understand why.' She raised her dark head. 'The minute I walked into the room I could sense an atmosphere of intimacy between you. I thought you were her lover, someone she'd never told me about, and I was just knocked back by all the emotions I felt. Jealousy, anger, sexual attraction. I thought you were gorgeous, just totally superb. . .'

'Oh, God!' he said, laughing, his body relaxing and his eyes glittering as he bent his head, his mouth close to hers. 'I've waited so long to hear you say you found me attractive, my darling! I thought you were so hooked on Radcliffe. . .blond, thin, uncomplicated, trendy. No ambition, no drive, no sex appeal. He's everything I'm not!'

'You can say that again!' she murmured, giving him a hot look through her lashes.

He smiled slowly, then drawled, 'You can't imagine how jealous I was of him. It became an obsession in the end. I just kept thinking, I don't believe it. I don't bloody believe it! Here she is, my dream woman, and she's madly in love with some young blond boy whose only ambition is to drive around in a sports car and drink champagne!'

'Tony's always been just a friend to me,' she said, smiling.

He stared at her, his face darkening. 'Don't call him Tony, either,' he said thickly. 'I can't stand it.'

'Darling, you have no need to be jealous of him.'

'Yes, I do,' he said, his mouth hard. 'You're not in love with him and you don't want to go to bed with him, but you do love him. Don't you?'

'As a friend, yes, but——'

'Rachel, I know it's unreasonable,' he said thickly. 'But I can't cope with the way I feel about you, not where Radcliffe's concerned. I've never been jealous in my life, not until I met you. It just caught me by the scruff of the neck and practically hammered my guts out. You have no idea how it felt, that first week we were back in Hong Kong. I was alone here night after night, and that sports car just kept driving up to get you. Every time I heard him blast his horn I wanted to kill him. I took it personally in the end, very personally. I began to wonder if he was doing it deliberately, if he knew I was insanely in love with you and thought it was funny to goad me.' He laughed and shook his dark head. 'Crazy, I know, but I really did begin to think it!'

'What shall I call him, then,' she said huskily, 'if not Tony?'

'Radcliffe!' he said bitingly, then laughed again, his face darkly flushed. 'I know it sounds absurd, but please do it for me or I might go out of my mind again, and really smash the living daylights out of him!'

'It doesn't sound absurd,' she said softly, touching his hard cheek. 'It sounds like a mirror image of me. I never felt jealous either, never believed I would be. But Domino. . .oh, Damian, why did you keep telling me you were sleeping with her? I nearly went insane; I wanted to come screaming round here night after night, hammer on your door and tell you to stop seeing her. . .'

'It was my only defence,' he said. 'I just didn't have any other way of stopping you guessing that I was in love with you. I thought it was so glaringly obvious. I mean—there I was, staring at you obsessively, unable to keep my hands off you, continually finding ways to be alone with you and then—the biggest give-away of all—actually proposing marriage to you!' He laughed. 'I couldn't believe you fell for that total fairy-tale of me wanting to get my hands on Swift Investments! I kept waiting in dread for someone to tap you on the shoulder and say, "By the way, you know Damian is chairman of Flint Investments International!"'

'Nobody did!' she said, incredulous.

'Well, they all knew,' he drawled. 'Every last one of them!'

She stared. 'Even my father?'

'Of course he knew,' Damian said. 'Why do you think he let me take the firm over? Because he knew I could handle it, he knew I wouldn't rip him off, and he knew I'd automatically get treated with respect everywhere I went in the world to represent the company.'

'But why didn't he tell me?'

'Well, I imagine, darling, that you never asked.' He studied her with those incredibly gorgeous blue eyes, filled with charm and love, darkness and intelligence, sex appeal and strength.

Rachel felt breathless, said softly, 'But I believed the stuff about Swift because you kept throwing it at me.'

'Ah. . .' he said softly. 'Well, that's all down to our incredibly exciting conversation on the plane.'

She looked up through her lashes. 'Oh, did you find it exciting too?'

'Intolerably exciting,' he said, kissing her cheek. 'It was the first bit of luck I'd had since I first set eyes on you. After you'd totally devastated me by saying you didn't find me remotely attractive, I was left racking my brains to think of a way to change your mind. That's why I called Domino and spoke to her deliberately in that seductive way.'

She caught her breath. 'You rat. . . I fell for that!'

'Well, I had to do something!' he drawled coolly. 'To ram it home to you in no uncertain terms that I was sexually active, and very much considered desirable by other women.'

'You certainly did that!' she said huskily. 'I was jealous of Domino before I even met her!'

'Yes, but I didn't know that,' he pointed out, brows lifting. 'All I had to go on was the very clear excitement you displayed in that conversation on the plane. I could see you were prickling from head to foot with some kind of emotion towards me. And I kept staring at you and thinking, My God, she's everything I've been looking for. You were so intelligent, so funny, so witty. . . I wanted to kiss your brains out.'

'You almost did!' she murmured, smiling. 'I was terrified when you pushed the seat back for me.'

'I needed some physical contact with you,' he drawled. 'I was fiercely aroused the whole time we were talking. When you backed off and said you wanted to sleep, I was so disappointed! I wanted to talk to you for the whole journey, but I couldn't let you know that, so I just sat there thinking, I've got to touch her. . . I've got to touch her. . .and then you tried to recline your seat.' He arched wicked black brows. 'As I said — I always take opportunities when I see them!'

'You stopped my heart when you took that particular opportunity. . .'

'And you gave me my strategy,' he said softly. 'I sat up all through the flight putting it together. I knew three things, by then. One: that you were sexually attracted to me but fighting it. Two: that you found my mind as exciting as I certainly found yours. And three: that you thought I was an ambitious sharpie trying to steal your father's company.' He flashed his blue eyes and smiled. 'When I dropped you at your villa, I went straight to the hospital and told your father I wanted you to come and work for me.'

'You didn't!'

'I'm afraid I did, my darling,' he drawled. 'I knew Charles wanted me to marry you for reasons we hardly need discuss. But that was just a hope he'd been tossing at me for a couple of years without any interest from me. I hadn't picked up on it, and he had no hand at all in your coming to work for me. That was strictly my idea. It was the only thing I could think of to get and keep you close to me — close enough for the attraction to grow.'

'I fought it so hard. . .'

'I could see you grappling with it on a daily basis,' he drawled softly. 'That first day you came to work for me, you were shaking with it when I untied your pony-tail and ran my fingers through your hair.'

'Oh, God. . .!' she groaned, blushing like mad and lowering her head to hide her face in his chest.

'Darling, I can assure you I was watching you like a hawk for any sign of it,' he said, kissing her bent head. 'And deliberately provoking it whenever I could without making myself obvious.'

She frowned, dark jealousy filling her soul, and said thickly, 'But you took Domino for lunch that day and——'

'Let me tell you a little bit about Domino,' he cut in deeply. 'She's been my secretary for two years, is quiet and reserved and madly in love with the man she lives with. He's a doctor, a Chinese guy, works out in the New Territories, saves lives on a daily basis and gets paid very little for his considerable sacrifices and hard work. Domino works for me in order to help support him. Also——' He paused, studying her. 'Her mother really is seriously ill.'

She gave a jerky nod, trying to combat her jealousy, knowing it was unreasonable, unjust, yet feeling it burn inside her, unstoppable and intolerable.

'Don't be jealous, darling,' he said softly, stroking her hair. 'I only see her at the office. She's efficient and hard-working and never bothers me when I'm busy.'

'I know, but——'

'I should never have made up those stories about her, I know, and I'm sorry, darling. But it just grew out of all proportion. You were so convinced she was my mistress and I couldn't deny it without giving myself away. In the end, I deliberately threw her at you because I was desperate for a sign of jealousy from you. The wedding day was hurtling towards us, and still you seemed crazy about Radcliffe. I was getting megawatts of sexual response from you, but nothing emotional, nothing—Radcliffe got it all. I felt as though I was being hung, drawn and quartered for my past, and the only way to live with what was happening to me was to try desperately to provoke some emotional reaction in you. The only thing that ever seemed to hit was letting you think she was my lover.'

'Don't ever be anyone's lover but mine!' she said in a shaking voice. 'I couldn't stand it, Damian. I'd lose control, go berserk. . .'

'That's my girl!' he said softly, smiling.

Her heart melted. She smiled, saying huskily, 'You rotten swine! How could you do that to me? I went through such hell. . .imagining you together. . .imagining you making love to her. . .'

'I had to stop you guessing,' he said, laughing softly. 'I was in love with you up to my neck from day one and you were seeing Radcliffe night after night, rejecting me day after day.'

She leant weakly against him. 'Darling. . .'

'I can't tell you how I felt the night it finally happened!' he said suddenly, his voice unsteady. 'The night we kissed for the first time. It was exquisite. I just stood there, my heart banging like a sledge-hammer, and watched it slowly dawning on you. Your eyes were darting all over me, you could barely speak, your face was burning up with heat. . .'

'It rushed through me. . .' she admitted huskily.

'And when I kissed you it rushed through *me*, waves of it; I could barely restrain myself, thought I was going to make love to you on the spot. But of course I had to back off because you pulled out of it, and started fighting again.'

'I'd never felt anything like it in my life,' she confessed. 'I had no idea how to cope with it.'

'You were frightened,' he said deeply, and she nodded. He stroked her hair. 'When did you realise just how serious it really was? In Auckland?'

Rachel whispered, 'Yes. . .'

'The nightmare.' His blue eyes studied her as they leant together against the french windows in the sunlight.

'I was fighting the way I felt, but I knew deep inside what was happening to me.'

He gave a wry smile. 'And now you're going to finally tell me what the nightmare was. . .?'

Rachel flushed, and lowered her lashes, telling him every detail.

'I knew it,' he said deeply, kissing her. 'I knew it was about me. I just didn't know how deep it had gone for you. I knew the attraction was very serious, but I also thought you were experienced. When you had the nightmare, I assumed it was because you'd had a lot of men without ever reaching any kind of genuine ecstasy with them.' He laughed and drawled, 'If you know what I mean!'

She frowned and tilted her head.

'No,' he said thickly, laughing. 'Wake up, Flint! She hasn't got a clue!'

Hot colour rushed up her face. 'I — I might have. I — I think I've read articles. . .'

'You're on the right track,' he said softly. 'But I wasn't. Not in Auckland, not the night I finally — oh, God, *finally* — got you on a bed. . .'

'I was so afraid of what was happening,' she said wryly. 'When you asked me to come into your bedroom my heart was beating so fast I thought it was going to come leaping out!'

'Mine, too!' he said under his breath. 'I got you on the bed and just lost my head completely. You'll never know how nearly I took you that night. I was in the most exquisite kind of agony, unable to think of anything but making love to you, and then I was pushing your skirt up and getting my face slapped. It knocked me straight out of paradise and back into reality.' He laughed. 'And what a reality! A virgin. . . my God, I could barely pull my shattered wits together. I stayed up all night trying to think, and all the time Radcliffe was there in my head like a demon, telling me you didn't care about me. Then when I proposed the next day, and made you tell me exactly how far you'd gone with other men — '

'No further than a kiss!' she said, turning scarlet.

'I don't know how I remained standing,' he said softly. 'I thought I was going to just keel over on to your shoulder and blurt it out: I love you, I love you. . .'

'Darling!' she said huskily, her eyes filled with love.

'I knew it was real then, Rachel. I knew it was a two-way thing. The problem was that you didn't know. Your inexperience told me that you must be in love with me — but I couldn't be sure. It was equally possible that you had never been forced to respond to a man before.'

'I'd never wanted to respond to a man before!'

His eyes darkened. 'But I'd provoked it. Deliberately. Don't forget I was already insanely jealous of Radcliffe. I could see he wasn't the type to try to seduce a virgin. Especially not someone he'd known all his life. I figured he was waiting for you to wake up, Sleeping-Beauty-style, at which point he'd marry you and make very tender love to you.'

'There's never been any kind of attraction between me and To——' She stopped, seeing the darkness in his eyes and understanding it. 'Between me and Radcliffe,' she amended softly.

He closed his eyes and held her against him, his mouth against her neck. 'I love you. . .'

'There's never been anything between me and Radcliffe,' she said huskily. 'Nor any of his friends. I think that's why I was so frightened of you.'

He lifted his head, a hard smile on his mouth.

Rachel smiled too. 'I'd always hung around with boys, never really known any men—certainly no man had ever made me feel and think the dreadful things I felt and thought whenever I saw you!'

His eyes darkened further. 'Such as?' he murmured unsteadily.

She flushed hotly. 'I. . . I kept wondering what you'd look like without your shirt.'

His heart started to thud rapidly. 'When was this?'

'The first night you kissed me,' she confessed huskily. 'And it wasn't deliberate. It just leapt up like a demon in my head when I was staring at you. . .like X-ray eyes. . . I was so shocked—and so excited.'

'And you've never felt that before,' he asked thickly, 'or since, with any other man?'

'Never.'

He drew a ragged breath. 'I told you it was rare.
Didn't I? I kept trying to make you see that something
exceptional was happening, but I couldn't tell you
straight out because love, my darling, left me without
defence. I'd already put my life on the line by marrying
you when I thought you were in love with Radcliffe.
All I could do was keep dropping hints, trying to get it
through to you that we were going through something
incredible together.'

'I didn't understand that until the wedding night
itself.'

'Is that why you tried to run out on me?'

She nodded, eyes darkening. 'I knew if you made
love to me I'd be lost. . .drowning. . .beyond help.'

'I couldn't believe it when you made a break for the
door!' he admitted. 'I was so shocked. Then you started
to fight me and I felt this red mist explode in front of
my eyes. To go through all of that, to keep my hands
off you for weeks, and then be refused on the wedding
night!'

'I remember!' she teased. 'Our frantic scuffle all over
the bedroom!'

'I blew every gasket in my head!' he admitted deeply.
'Except one. The love gasket. I was angry enough that
night to rape you, but I was also very deeply in love,
and I wanted more than anything else to make love to
you. Real love. The kind of lovemaking I'd practically
dedicated my life to experiencing.'

Her lashes flickered. 'You told Jenny that——'

'Yes,' he said softly. 'An erotic expression of the
soul through the body. I'd told myself for weeks that
our wedding night would be such a moving experience
for both of us that you'd suddenly realise you were in

love with me, and tell me, and everything would end happily ever after.'

'And I did admit to myself that I was in love with you that night,' she said huskily. 'It was incredible. . . barriers were crashing down all around. But I thought you were so experienced that it wouldn't have affected you as it did me.'

'My God, no,' he said, his eyes deeply serious. 'If anything, it probably made it even more moving. I was drowning in you, I couldn't breathe with it. . .'

'I remember,' she said softly, looking through her lashes at his strong face. 'You were incoherent at the end. . .'

'And I kept saying your name.' He smiled. 'I had to express what I was feeling. I couldn't just keep silent. It was the most exceptional emotional and physical experience of my life, and I had to say something. . . so I said, Rachel. . . Rachel. . .but inside the words were, I love you. . . I love you. . .'

Rachel buried her face in his neck.

He stroked her hair, murmuring, 'I would never have said it, you know. Not without hearing it from you first.'

Her lashes flickered and she raised her head. 'Are you serious?'

'Deadly serious.' He studied her with a cool smile. 'I took my life in my hands as it was just now — telling you so much about myself and my life.'

'But I was so sure you were leading up to saying it!'

'No,' he said softly, ' I was leading up to *you* saying it!'

Her lips parted in a shocked smile.

Damian studied her with loving amusement and murmured, 'You don't really believe I would have knelt to you? Ever? Regardless of the circumstances, or how I felt, or how much I needed to tell you that I loved you?'

Rachel studied his strong, handsome face for a moment, then said huskily, 'No. . .'

He smiled, black lashes flickering, then said softly, 'Come to bed.'

As they walked inside, arm in arm, she said huskily, 'Darling, what would you have done if I hadn't said it first?'

'I don't know,' he answered deeply, leading her up the stairs, his face serious. 'Got out of it somehow, I suppose. I've been so afraid for so long that you'd never care for me. . . I couldn't have said it. I knew I had to bring it to some kind of confession, but saying, "I love you," to a woman who loved another man? Absolutely no way on God's earth!'

'Of course not. . .' she agreed.

'All I could do,' he drawled, 'was keep talking, just keep telling you who I really was, what really went on inside my head, and hope that you sensed the barriers coming down very slowly for you to get in and say it. But if you hadn't said it, Rachel. . .those barriers would have slammed back up and locked into place again.'

'No more barriers,' she said huskily. 'Darling, I want everything you are. I can't bear to think of what would have happened if I hadn't told you. Just think of the hell we would have been through. . .'

'Yes,' he said deeply, 'we would have had to carry on as we were. I wouldn't have let you go without a fight, though, even if the hell had driven you to it. I still won't, if you ever want to try and leave me.' His eyes were dark as he led her into the bedroom and closed the door behind them. 'I never thought I'd feel that way about any woman, but it is how I feel about you.'

Rachel stood with him, her hands on his shoulders, below the overhead fan. 'I never thought I'd feel this way about a man,' she said, her face serious. 'But you've taken me so deep I feel as though I'm complete for the first time. As though intense emotions — jealousy, rage, unreasoning desire — are all the parts of me that have always been missing.'

'The necessary components of love, my darling, are apparently as dark and fathomless as the reasons we're alive in the first place. But at least we can express them all when we make love, release them in a fierce cross-current, emotional, mental and physical unity.'

They walked to the bed, hand in hand, slid on to it.

'Rachel. . .' he said suddenly, frowning.

She caught her breath, touched by the uncertainty in his eyes. 'Yes, darling. . .what is it?'

'This may not last forever. You do realise that, don't you?'

Pain struck at her heart and she said thickly, 'I. . . I suppose nothing lasts forever, but ——'

'I mean the overwhelming desire we currently feel for each other,' he said softly. 'It's not necessarily going to be present in our relationship for the rest of our lives. Darling, it couldn't possibly be!' He gave a husky laugh, kissed her mouth gently. 'We'd be exhausted. I'd die of a heart attack. We both would.' He studied her intensely, his smile fading. 'Love is what will hold us together. It's what we have — isn't it? Beyond everything else — beyond anger, beyond jealousy, beyond desire. There's love, pure and simple.'

Rachel smiled. 'I can't imagine not wanting you to make love to me, but I understand what you're saying.'

'I hope you do,' he said deeply. 'Because I want children.'

Her eyes filled with tears of hope. 'Darling. . .' She fell against his chest. 'So do I. . .!'

Damian stroked her hair. 'I want to be with you for the rest of my life. Not just while we're still hopelessly in love with each other, but after that, too. When you're used to me.' He laughed deeply, kissing the top of her head. 'When you catch me eating cottage cheese straight from the fridge at three in the morning! When I'm watching rugby on the TV and the children are running about like savages, screaming for attention. When every fixed point on the map has been obliterated by the years we've spent together, and we wonder how the hell we ever met. . .' He lifted her head, studied her with those warm, intelligent, dark, sexy eyes. 'I want you to love me through all of that.'

'I've loved you through all of this,' she said huskily. 'How could I do anything other than love you more as we grow older?'

'It's not an easy thing, though it should be, to be in love.'

She laughed softly. 'It's such hell, isn't it? Getting to the point where nothing matters except hearing those words. . . I love you.'

He gave a deep sigh, lowering his dark head to hers. 'No. Nothing else matters but that.'

He kissed her then, his mouth warm and sensitive to her every response, and when she put her arms around his neck he gave a hoarse inhalation of breath, his arms tightening around hers, and the kiss took fire, grew passionate, their bodies pressing together, harder, harder. . .

'Oh, God. . .!' he said thickly. 'Rachel. . .'

'I hate you!' she whispered as they fell back on to

the bed. 'How could you put me through such hell. . .?'
Her body arched against him. 'Touch me, touch
me. . .'

He gave a harsh intake of breath, his hands moving
over her, and as they made love in a fierce celebration
of the overwhelming emotions they felt so deeply for
one another Rachel knew that this ungoverned passion
was love.

ESCAPE INTO ANOTHER WORLD...

...With Temptation Dreamscape Romances

Two worlds collide in 3 very special Temptation titles, guaranteed to sweep you to the very edge of reality.

The timeless mysteries of reincarnation, telepathy and earthbound spirits clash with the modern lives and passions of ordinary men and women.

Available November 1993   Price £5.55

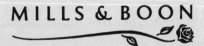

MILLS & BOON

Next Month's Romances

Each month you can choose from a wide variety of romance with Mills & Boon. Below are the new titles to look out for next month, why not ask either Mills & Boon Reader Service or your Newsagent to reserve you a copy of the titles you want to buy – just tick the titles you would like and either post to Reader Service or take it to any Newsagent and ask them to order your books.

Please save me the following titles:	Please tick	√
DAWN SONG	Sara Craven	
FALLING IN LOVE	Charlotte Lamb	
MISTRESS OF DECEPTION	Miranda Lee	
POWERFUL STRANGER	Patricia Wilson	
SAVAGE DESTINY	Amanda Browning	
WEST OF BOHEMIA	Jessica Steele	
A HEARTLESS MARRIAGE	Helen Brooks	
ROSES IN THE NIGHT	Kay Gregory	
LADY BE MINE	Catherine Spencer	
SICILIAN SPRING	Sally Wentworth	
A SCANDALOUS AFFAIR	Stephanie Howard	
FLIGHT OF FANTASY	Valerie Parv	
RISK TO LOVE	Lynn Jacobs	
DARK DECEIVER	Alex Ryder	
SONG OF THE LORELEI	Lucy Gordon	
A TASTE OF HEAVEN	Carol Grace	

If you would like to order these books in addition to your regular subscription from Mills & Boon Reader Service please send £1.80 per title to: Mills & Boon Reader Service, Freepost, P.O. Box 236, Croydon, Surrey, CR9 9EL, quote your Subscriber No:................................... (If applicable) and complete the name and address details below. Alternatively, these books are available from many local Newsagents including W.H.Smith, J.Menzies, Martins and other paperback stockists from 3 December 1993.

Name:..

Address:..

....Post Code:..........................

To Retailer: If you would like to stock M&B books please contact your regular book/magazine wholesaler for details.

You may be mailed with offers from other reputable companies as a result of this application. If you would rather not take advantage of these opportunities please tick box ☐